I

ENGINEERING

INVITATION SERIES

Invitation to Economics   David Whynes
Invitation to Engineering   Eric Laithwaite
Invitation to Linguistics   Richard Hudson
Invitation to Politics   Michael Laver
Invitation to Social Work   Bill Jordan
Invitation to Statistics   Gavin Kennedy

Other titles in preparation

Invitation to Anthropology   Maurice Bloch
Invitation to Archaeology   Philip Rahtz
Invitation to Astronomy   Jacqueline and Simon
                                   Mittom
Invitation to Industrial Relations Tom Keenoy
Invitation to Management   Peter Lawrence
Invitation to Nursing   June Clark
Invitation to Philosophy   Martin Hollis
Invitation to Psychology   Philip Johnson-Laird
Invitation to the Sciences   Barry Barnes
Invitation to Teaching   Trevor Kerry

Invitation to ENGINEERING

Eric Laithwaite

BASIL BLACKWELL

© Eric Laithwaite, 1984

First published 1984
Basil Blackwell Publisher Ltd
108 Cowley Road, Oxford OX4 1JF, UK

Basil Blackwell Inc.
432 Park Avenue South, Suite 1505,
New York, NY 10016, USA

British Library Cataloguing in Publication Data
Laithwaite, E.R.
    Invitation to engineering.
    1. Engineering
    I. Title
    620   TA145

    ISBN 0-85520-661-6
    ISBN 0-85520-662-4 Pbk

Typeset by Katerprint Co Ltd, Oxford
Printed in Great Britain by
T. J. Press Ltd, Padstow.

Contents

Preface

It is only rarely that young people of eighteen or nineteen really know what they hope to be doing by the time they are thirty. The help they receive in schools has increased enormously in the past fifty years, and a 'careers adviser' among the staff is now usual, rather than rare.

Nevertheless there are very few ex-engineers teaching physics in schools even to the 'engineering science' courses introduced in the late 1960s and early 1970s. Physics teachers who are themselves physicists can at best have but a superficial knowledge of an engineering career, no matter how many refresher courses they attend nor how many leaflets and brochures they read.

Invitation to Engineering has therefore been written to give as good an insight as possible into what the daily life of a practising engineer is really like, whether it be in industry, with its many facets, or as an academic, including consulting involvement with industry. Any sixth-former who has opted for science subjects or fifth-former who is more interested in the science side than the arts, *must* read this book, which could easily be the one act that determines the shape of his or her future.

Engineering is both exciting and demanding. It is a challenge as great as any major geographical exploration into the unknown. At the same time it offers at least as great an opportunity to improve the lot of humans on earth as does any other single profession.

I am much indebted to Sue Corbett and Kim Pickin of

Blackwell's for discussions during the preparation of the manuscript. On more than one occasion they gave me a fresh vigour that prevented me from 'going stale', which is so easy to do when writing about a subject with which one is so familiar. They also gave me invaluable assistance with the planning and arrangement of the book.

1

What is Engineering?

'The engineer views hopefully the hitherto unattainable'
*(Inscription on the Lamme Medal of The Institute of
Electrical and Electronics Engineers, USA)*

Often the best way to answer a question is by describing
something relevant to it and giving the reader the message
less directly. After all, it is going to take me a whole book to
answer this question and even then I shall by no means have
done it fully. But the following quotation says all I want to
say by way of introduction:

Should you decide to enter the engineering profession,
your employers, if they are sensible, will say to you:

You are a young engineer entering a brave new world. We shall do
our best to tell you how we do things now. But in a few years we
shall expect you to tell us what we have to do. We cannot afford to
stand still, and we rely on you and your fellows to keep us in the van
of progress (Say, 1965).

The word 'engineer' comes from the French word *'ingén-
ieur'* (or these days, *ingénieure*) which literally means 'an
ingenious one' and to this extent we are all engineers at one
time or another, when we display ingenuity in whatever
context. But then, if we remove a thorn from our thumb, are
we not in the same way surgeons for the moment?

A professional engineer has been specially trained to use his
powers of observation, his curiosity and his experience, as

1

well as his ingenuity in order to solve problems that others have failed to solve. The basic requirements for an engineer are mathematics and science, without which he has virtually no tools and stands helpless before almost any real problem.

Let me right at the beginning resolve an embarrassment only caused by the English language. There is no impersonal pronoun that means both 'he' and 'she' at the same time. To use 'they' is to lose the punch of the personal approach and since engineering is *in every way* just as much a profession for women as for men, will you please read 'he' or 'she' whenever the word 'he' appears? The only reason for choosing 'he' is that at present the profession is very much male-dominated. It *is* one of the aims of this book to change just that. If the reader is indeed a young lady, then I would say to you that the fact that you have chosen to read the first page makes it particularly important that you read this book right to the end. You will then see that engineering is not just made up of lumps that you stub your toes on, but could very well be described as a series of processes that affect us all.

True, there are spanners and oil cans and boiler suits; they are all part of the great mixture, but they are used and worn by the skilled people who are directed, guided and consulted by the engineers with clean hands who handle pencils and pocket calculators. They also have light pens and all the modern aids that their own profession has provided. These days, some of the skilled people operate the light pens and computer keyboards, as well as the spanners.

There is no doubt, of course, that science is the very bedrock on which engineering is founded. Yet an engineer is also an artist, having much in common with the true artist in that when all else fails, intuition and inspiration will be all that is left to solve a problem that cannot wait. The great Victorian engineer Osborne Reynolds often used the word 'art' when he meant 'engineering', as when he gave a Cantor lecture at the Society of Arts (Reynolds, 1883):

I have to deal with facts, and I shall try to deal with nothing but facts. Many of these facts, or the conclusions to be immediately drawn from them, may appear to bear on the possibilities—or, rather the impossibilities—of art. But in the Society of Arts I need not point out that art knows no limit; where one way is found to be closed, it is the function of art to find another. Science teaches us the results that will follow from a known condition of things; but there is always the unknown condition, the future effect of which no science can predict. You must have heard of the statement in 1837, that a steam voyage across the Atlantic was a physical impossibility, which was said to have been made by Dr. Lardner. What Dr. Lardner really stated, according to his own showing, was that such a voyage exceeded the then present limits of steam power. In this he was within the mark, as anyone would be if he were to say now that communication between England and America exceeded the limit of the power of the telephone. But to use such an argument against a proposed enterprise, is to ignore the development of art to which such an enterprise may lead.

What a splendid introduction this paragraph makes to any treatise on engineering. See how he puts pure science in its proper place as a guide but never a master. See optimism flowing from his pen as he forecasts confidently the trans-atlantic telephone cable, still some time away. See him condemn the present-day accountant who advises the banker against putting up money for a project 'known to be impossible'. How Reynolds would have loved the Space Age with just the kind of spin-off that his last sentence forecasts. Who could have predicted that the problem of re-entering the earth's atmosphere would lead to the development of a ceramic nose cone whose material would within a few years be used in the electric cookers of the average household? Reynolds would have been the first to declare that it was 95% engineering that put Armstrong on the moon and only 5% science.

Like many other famous engineers, he never accepted defeat.

Sir Peter Medawar (1969), in his excellent little book *Induction and Intuition in Scientific Thought,* drew a quick sketch of a scientist in these words:

A scientist is a man who weighs the earth and ascertains the temperature of the sun. He destroys matter and invents new forms of matter and one day he will invent new forms of life.

I would like, modestly, to attempt a paraphrase of that sketch as it applies to an engineer, thus:

An engineer is a man who *uses* the earth and tries to capture the sun's energy more effectively. He controls the *rate* of destruction of matter and tries to find alternative sources of energy and new materials. He invents new *shapes* of matter and strives to improve the *quality* of life in whatever form he finds it.

So broad is the extent of engineering that one is perhaps entitled to ask: 'Is anything in science NOT engineering?' and I think the answer is that it *used* to be, and some of this is illustrated in Sir Peter's sketch above. The scientists who originally weighed the earth and measured the temperature of the sun did it out of sheer curiosity. It was to be knowledge for its own sake, without any thought of putting it to use. This is *not* engineering. But these days, the pure scientists are enlightened and they too see the need for their findings to be used as well as merely catalogued as facts, although I must confess that I still classify researching the origin of the universe as science for its own sake and not very usable when you have got it! But I hope I am wrong.

Engineering is, and always has been, a challenge. It is exciting and for many of us it has the enchantment of first walking on new snow or of discovering an entirely new flower. It has fascinated men since they first tried to cross deep water by lashing together logs of wood to make a raft. Engineering made possible the Industrial Revolution and continues to improve the lot of mankind on earth at an ever-increasing rate.

It is only in the name that there is confusion, and this has largely arisen out of politics and the popular media. Journalists will speak of 'applied science' when they mean 'engineering'; they will use the word 'technology' which is a blanket word covering engineering and other things. This is a pity, because it was picked up by politicians who commonly spoke of science and technology, thereby implying that there was *no* science in technology. One even sees 'engineering science' which always reminds me of describing Fido as an 'animal dog'. But 'technology' also does engineering a disservice in that it embraces the crafts, which are considered un-clever in academic circles and especially in the scientific Establishment, and this has led to the legend that engineering is a 'soft option' for sixth-formers not clever enough to read physics or mathematics or chemistry or medicine at a university. 'Technology', more than perhaps any other word, has been the means of preventing the engineer from becoming a 'professional man' in the eyes of the BBC and therefore of the public.

Worst of all perhaps, so many school teachers are still badly misinformed about engineering and the old image still remains, 'Smith did brilliantly in his "A" levels and is going to Cambridge to read natural sciences. You didn't do too well, did you, Robinson? Still you can always do engineering.' Somehow this has to stop. Engineers are the backbone of this and many other countries. They control all the public services and the major manufacturing industries. They do not belong to a union and they do not go on strike. They are not to be confused with mechanics, electricians, plumbers and woodworkers, excellent jobs though all these people do. All the latter are tradespeople, with a strict enough training of their own. They are professionals of their own kind. But they do not have a Royal Charter and are not entitled to call themselves chartered engineers.

Perhaps the only true recognition of the place in society occupied by engineers is in the small matter of signing passports. A member of the public wanting a passport seeks out a 'special' person to sign his or her form and the back of one of the photographs (the so-called likeness!). Again it is a popular misconception that this special person must be a clergyman or a judge or magistrate or doctor. Not an engineer, surely?—Yes, a chartered electrical engineer is to be classed with the professionals in this ability and many is the time my services have been refused by friends clutching their application forms tightly in case I were to mutilate them with my 'unofficial' signature!

This is not 'sour grapes' on my part. It is something that must be put right in the national interest, and if the school teachers are not aware of it, then the sixth-formers will just have to teach them!

MONEY

However distasteful it may sound on first reading, engineering is basically about making money and its closest ally is economics.

But there are all kinds of money. *Knowledge* is money in its own right. Inventions are money, especially when patented. But in addition to legal documents such as patents there has arisen, largely in this century and in the USA, a commodity called 'know-how' that cannot be tied down legally, nor have fixed monetary values set upon it. It reminds one more of the kind of commodities sold in eastern bazaars, where getting the best price is a matter for verbal bargaining. But the commodity is real enough, even though it almost defies description. 'Making things work', 'knowing how it *really* works' and similar expressions go some of the way but are never adequate. Lester Taylor wrote a splendid book called *Making Electric Things Happen* (Taylor, 1967), which gives as good an insight into the engineering profession as I have ever seen. If I succeed in equalling his book I shall be more than content and even then you must read it as a companion volume. Get it from a library, if it is out of print.

The engineer has but a single purpose after all. It is TO SIFT THE PROFITABLE FROM THE LESS PROFITABLE. There are two distinct sides to this. It can be done in terms of hardware, or in terms of concepts. In hardware can be included inventing a cheaper process, or a quicker one, or one which uses more readily available materials, or makes less noise or is less polluting. The list is incredibly long, but the final answer is always *profit in cash*; rarely for the engineers themselves, generally for their employers.

Those who seek the profitable in concepts are often academics, but not necessarily so. With the advent of computers profitability in concepts became inextricably linked to profitability in hard cash again, but happily there will always be the true academic who seeks elegance of solution for its own sake and needs another person to recognise just what he or she has done. History is full of stories of great men whose work was not fully appreciated until others 'translated' it: Faraday, Maxwell, Heaviside, Tesla, and there are lesser giants today, much valued by industry, many of whom reside in universities, who go out into the wilderness alone, and when they have companions who appreciate enough of what they are doing their work may be immediately applicable to engineering practice.

There is a real place for the academically minded in engineering. The image of the man in the 'ivory tower' has gone. Perhaps science fiction has helped to make a hero out of one who used to be an object of fun. Whatever it was, it was long overdue. It is one of my aims in writing this book to make more people aware of the potential of an engineering career in whatever sphere of life it is practised.

Engineering is practised, as law is practised and as medicine and surgery are practised; and although on the surface it does seem to be concerned mostly with hardware, it is surprising just how much of it is about people. After all, for whom is the hardware intended? Doesn't the customer's opinion matter? An engineer's daily life can, if that particular engineer so chooses, be as personally involved with the general public as is that of the average general practitioner.

There are so many different forms of engineering, and so many different ways in which it is needed, that it is going to take me many chapters to show you even the major facets of it all. But I hope that I shall always keep you aware of the challenge, the excitement, the job satisfaction, the companionship and the other rewards that go with it, whatever aspect of the subject appeals to you most. At the end I hope you will be convinced that: 'Here, at least, is a job worthwhile.'

REFERENCES

Medawar, P. B. (1969) *Induction and Intuition in Scientific Thought* (1968 Jayne Lectures of the American Philosophical Society). London, Methuen

Reynolds, O. (1883) *The Transmission of Energy,* Cantor Lecture delivered to the Society of Arts, 23 April 1883. (Published in his *Papers on Mechanical and Physical Subjects, Vol. II, 1881–1900,* Cambridge, CUP, 1901)

Say, M. G. (1965) *Electrical and Electronic Engineering—A Professional Career.* London, The Institution of Electrical Engineers

Taylor, P. L. (1967) *Making Electric Things Happen.* Reading, Berkshire, Educational Explorers

2

The Evolution of Engineering

'And God said, Let there be light.' (*Genesis*, 1, iv)

It is often said in high places that engineers exploit the discoveries of scientists and use them for making profit. It is even implied sometimes that this is *all* they do. Perhaps the simplest counter to this is that the pure sciences, as we now understand them, have a history that stretches back perhaps 200 years (in any concentrated form). Engineering, on the other hand, can be traced back some 30,000 years when primitive men tied logs together with reed ropes to make rafts, and soon learned to harness the wind by putting masts and sails on them.

That's it—*harnessing*—that's what engineering is—harnessing the natural forces on earth to man's advantage: the wind, the seas, the tides, the soil. Capturing the sun's energy in several ways. Making the desert blossom. In the process the engineer turns a hand to gardening, sailing, carpentry, farming, soldiering and many other apparently *different* professions.

Engineering is much more than that.

It is concerned with everyday living, often with survival, especially in its more ancient beginnings. Engineering is therefore concerned with common sense as well as ingenuity. When it finally brought affluence, at least to a minority, it was on the first rung of a ladder that it has been climbing ever since—improving the quality of life for all mankind. This involves not only harnessing, but *controlling,* the natural forces and resources.

Invitation to Engineering

An engineer looks at a volcano erupting and murmurs, somewhat shamefully: 'What a waste!'

BIOLOGICAL EVOLUTION

It is said that the great naturalist Alfred Russel Wallace, in a high fever in the Moluccas, visualised in a fortnight the whole process of evolution that had taken Darwin many years. Be that as it may, it is generally accepted that the natural process of evolution is based on the principle of 'natural selection' whereby small changes in colour or shape or habit of a creature give it advantage over other similar creatures such that its slightly modified form survives its fellows. The process is necessarily slow and there are few rapid jumps.

Nevertheless it has the ingredients of survival, profitability, change and progress which are all to be found in engineering. What it lacks is the interference of an external agent and the ability to make sudden leaps forward, to accelerate the whole process and finally to depart from it radically, as indeed engineering has done.

This is not to say that engineering did not have a remarkable resemblance to natural evolution, but of the sudden jump process one needs no better example than the result of the Battle of Hastings in 1066. Bio-engineer John Lenihan wrote of this event in the Eighth Kelvin Lecture to the Royal Philosophical Society on 27 March 1968—just a moment, what did you say John's profession was?—'bio-engineer'—we shall want to know more of him and his kind later on (pp. 57 and 83).

Two of the most significant and spectacular advances in the history of civilisation were accomplished by technology alone. The military, political and social revolution which culminated (or started) at the Battle of Hastings was precipitated by the introduction of the stirrup. Until the eighth century, a mounted soldier had the advantage of a better view but had to rely on his own muscle power and was helpless when unhorsed. Once provided with stirrups, however, his fighting power was greatly increased.

10

The horseman now merely held the lance between his arm and his body, allowing the muscle power of the horse to deliver the blow. The feudal system developed as a means of sharing the burden of providing horses and suitably equipped soldiers; the aristocracy enjoyed their lands in return for the obligation of serving the monarch, especially by providing fighting strength. The Franks absorbed and exploited the new technology of war. The Anglo-Saxons did not take it seriously and in 1066 they paid the price of their neglect.

Kenneth Clark in his excellent treatise on civilisation chose his own heroes and landmarks. Men such as Michelangelo were singled out as having influenced the course of human experience to a first degree. But none of these is ever to be placed in the same class as those nameless ones (for there were many) whose engineering skills shaped the blade of the plough.

It was a product of pure biological-type evolution, each generation modifying the shape and the size to give a better result—and not a physicist or mathematician in sight. Engineering today can sometimes be like that! It is interesting to note that despite the age of the computer there is still no equation to the shape of the plough blade. Yet this single implement raised the quality of life from one in which every man toiled long hours every day to wrest a living from the soil for himself and for his family to one in which a class society arose with an elite who could eventually afford to indulge in the luxury we now call 'science'!

The plough blade is an excellent example of another major facet of engineering—the study of *shape* and the study of *size*. Today we call them *topology* and *scaling*.

ENGINEERING EVOLUTION

If a biological evolution was soon outstripped by the interference of engineers with the natural processes (and apart from the plough blade this was what largely occurred) another kind of evolution with biological analogues occurred among the engineers themselves.

For thousands of years the primitive folk we now see as engineering pioneers never thought of themselves in such terms. There were seamen, farmers, soldiers and men of a few other occupations who could clearly be identified as leading quite different kinds of lives. But not until the Industrial Revolution did entirely new 'species' emerge, the men who made *machines*. They could be seen to be neither soldiers nor sailors, nor had they anything to do with the earth itself. They did not build roads, nor bridge rivers, and yet they had skills in common with those who did. History was witnessing the birth of the founder engineers, in biological terms the equivalent of the first mammals and the first birds. Today, we call the road and bridge builders 'civil engineers' (short for civilian engineers) and the machine makers 'mechanical engineers'.

Only beyond this stage did the process receive its first injection of science, from Arago and Oersted, Ampère, Volta and Faraday. Their quest for knowledge for its own sake laid the foundations for the third profession 'electrical engineering' to take its place as one of the 'Big Three' that constituted the engineering profession as a whole for nearly a century.

Why should engineers be interested in the history of their profession and its likeness to biological evolution? The answer to this lies in our rapidly changing world where problems of survival, very different from those of our primitive ancestors but nonetheless vital, demand that we be forewarned as to the way events are likely to go. Economic survival as a firm, or as a nation, national survival *per se*— these are the descendants of the individual's survival of the past. One of the ways of doing this is by examining the path of history even though it often throws only a little light on the subject. Its evolutionary equivalent illustrates the difficulty.

One is looking at an animal very like a lemur and trying to see what it might become. The great apes would appear at that time nothing short of science fiction, yet this animal was in fact their direct ancestor. Still we have to try even though we know of comparable changes within a century. Imagine the reaction to a newspaper headline of 1900 that declared, 'Before this century is out, we shall have cut inch steel plate with a beam of light; we shall travel by air at ten times the speed of sound; we shall be able to set up a three-dimensional image in New York of a man living in Australia, see him move, hear him speak. He will appear solid, alive, in New York.' All this and much more came to pass, as we know.

NATURAL GROWTH

In so far as knowledge could be said to be quantifiable we might reflect on how its growth compares with that of any living creature left to its own ways, unchecked by enemies of any kind. The latter tends to increase in such a way that not only is the rate of increase itself increasing, but the rate of the rate of increase also increases, and so on. The process might almost be called 'explosive'. From 30,000 years ago until perhaps AD 1800, the progress in engineering knowledge might well be compared with that of evolution, the only differences being the sudden jumps already described, which produced the stirrup, the horse collar, the horseshoe and biggest of all the plough. But what has happened since has been much more like a natural, unchecked, exponential growth such as occurred when the first rabbits were introduced into Australia.

If knowledge simply increased on a linear basis and we learned new techniques, produced new materials, new processes and new engineered products on the basis of twice as many in two years, three times as many in three years, and so on, we could look forward to a future little short of science fiction proportions for its sheer wonder. *But we are progressing much faster than that.* We cannot now see where the graph of rate of rate of increase of knowledge begins to straighten! Where might we be in 100 years if all this continues?

At a recent school speech day at which I was guest of honour, the headmaster, who was a natural orator, spoke for over an hour, but he was never dull. At one point he stared at all his pupils in the front of the hall and told them: 'Many of you sitting here tonight will live to be a hundred and twenty.' I reflected that he could have been in no way exaggerating, rather he might have been understating the case. Nor will the extra years be spent in wheelchairs or geriatric institutions. The face of education will change. We shall have so much more to learn that we shall be being educated all our lives and enjoying it. But remember that all this will be dependent on successful engineering.

It can be argued of course that there will be controls. Wars are often quoted as one of these. The history of wars has shown that in general the rate of technological, scientific and especially medical progress has accelerated during major wars rather than been slowed.

THE COMPUTER'S PREDICTION

After his retirement the late Dennis Gabor, Nobel Prize-winner for holography, joined other scientists and engineers in the United States and put together one of the most complex computer programs that has ever been compiled. They were attempting to predict what life on earth might really be like in the 21st century. They had attempted to quantify such aspects as pollution, where 100% pollution meant the extinction of all life, 30% meant 30% of all rivers contained no life, and so on. They even had a quantified facet labelled 'quality of life'. Things like average life span, population of the earth, average income were much more readily quantified. The interplay between racialism, nationalism, religion and politics was all built into the program. Like Professor Gibson's model of the Severn Estuary (see pp. 15 and 78) they fitted in figures from as far back in history as the figures were thought to be reliable from the records. Then they ran the program for a few hundred years and checked it to see how well it was doing in terms of what really happened. The program was then modified in the light of the obvious errors and re-run, and this process continued until the computer was getting it correct, right up to the then present time (the early 1970s). Then they let it run on!

Some most surprising results came out; some good, some bad. At the time there was a general panic about pollution.

14

The computer showed that at no time would the earth ever exceed 30% pollution and this item would stabilise itself. On the other hand it predicted that between the years 2020 and 2025, nine people out of ten throughout the world would die in a single year—from disease, not from weapons of war. Like the rabbits we were to have our myxomatosis—and like the rabbits, survive it.

Now of course this program was much more prone to errors than most, because of its complexity. Perhaps a conservative view of its findings might be: Yes, there *will* be controls, but they will not be the ones you might think. One of the clear lessons was that the graphs of world population, average life span, quality of life, pollution and many others passed through the two World Wars of this century with scarcely a noticeable kink!

For me the message was that as individuals we must all get on with doing our best at all times and that we ought to believe that mankind has a destiny, whatever the pessimists might say to the contrary. Our engineering will be ever-present, making vital contributions in all fields of human endeavour.

FASHION

Among the things that are not readily quantifiable in a computer program, nor predictable on any kind of physical law, because it depends in part on purely human whim, is the subject of fashion. We can begin by thinking about fashion in clothes, for this is the most common aspect to which the word is applied. The driving forces behind fashion are the human desire for change for its own sake, the avoidance of boredom. This is then exploited commercially for huge profits and the 'captains' of that industry tell the public what it wants and then sell it to them!

Now there are fashions in engineering, not quite so greed-motivated as in the 'rag trade', but certainly money-dominated to a large extent. The order of events usually takes this form.

In the beginning of a new subject, the first question is:

'Can it be done at all?'

At this stage no one questions the cost or why it is being attempted. Those who attempt it do it in the best traditions of all great explorers. Those who finance it do so in the best traditions of the great gamblers. But as soon as it is established that it can be done, the second question is almost obvious:

'How *well* can it be done?'

The accountant enters the new business and tells the engineer what needs to be done.

But the really intriguing part of engineering fashion is the definition of 'well' in the second question. By way of example I can perhaps do no better than to take my own specialist subject, that of electric motors and generators.

The first interpretation of 'well' is *efficiency*. By this I mean the scientific definition of efficiency which is the ratio of output power to input power. (Any other kind of efficiency should be specified, as in the ratio of energy output to energy input which is 'energy efficiency', and so on.) Designers of direct current motors of the latter half of the 19th century strove for 1% more in efficiency in an effort to beat their competitors. With hindsight, this was a form of accountancy-consciousness, but it was also a technique guilty of 'putting all its eggs in one basket' and an exposure of a far from adequate understanding of electrical machine technology, for it is always possible to go on increasing the efficiency of a motor of a given output simply by increasing its size and cost. So all the emphasis was being put on the running cost and none on the capital cost. No account was therefore taken of the depreciation on capital, of share prices, the stock market in general or anything except the 'in' word *efficiency*. It can therefore most properly be defined as 'fashion' in precisely the same context as that of the clothing industry.

Came the 1890s after alternating current machines had passed the first question, 'Can it be done at all?' (which was answered by Nikola Tesla in 1888) and a new fashion arose—

power factor. For the sake of non-electricals, the power in an electric circuit is always given by the product of voltage and current. But in alternating current work, these two quantities are varying as sine waves and the two may not always be in phase with each other. If the phase angle of difference is φ then the simple power calculation is extended to

$$\text{Power} = \text{volts} \times \text{amps} \times (\cos \varphi)$$

Cos φ is known as the 'power factor' and, of course, is always less than unity. Thus a machine with a power factor of 0.5 requires twice the current of a machine with a power factor of 1.0 and since the losses in a machine vary with the *square* of the current, the lower power factor machine has four times the losses, is less efficient and will need to be bigger to dissipate the losses and will therefore cost more. So power factor took over from efficiency, *per se,* as the fashionable quality of an electric motor during the first two decades of the present century.

But with the coming of a massive increase in road transport, followed by the rapid development in aircraft, came a demand for lightweight versions of many things, and certainly lighter electric motors and generators. The amount of power that could be produced from a given weight of machine or the 'power-to-weight ratio' superseded both efficiency and power factor as the fashionable commodity of the immediate pre-World War II years. With half the century gone the age of the accountant had come to stay, and return on capital investment became at least as important as running cost and 'power-to-cost ratio' came into fashion. Of course power/cost and power/weight ratios had a lot in common. A bigger motor needed a bigger crane to load it on to a bigger truck to take it to its site where a similar crane would lower it on to a bigger concrete base requiring more floor space, and all the extra sizes were costing money, right down to the state where a bigger can of paint was needed to paint the machine.

Power factor as a fashionable quantity seemed as far away as feather boas and crinolines. But a new invention was soon to change all that. In the 1950s the meteoric rise of the transistor relegated vacuum valves (triodes, tetrodes and pentodes) to the museums so far as electronic circuits were concerned within a quarter of a century, and the transistor was soon to be followed by the thyristor, the high-power solid state version of the transistor. 'Power electronics' was the new subject. The d.c. motor was now in its death throes, apart from battery-driven children's toys. Induction motors could now be run from variable frequency solid state power packs and achieve high efficiency speed control that had hitherto been impossible without rubbing contacts and brushes. There was just one slight snag. Power electronic circuits hated low power factor—more than that, would not tolerate it—and power factor correction equipment is expensive. Power factor in machines returned at least as a 'half-fashion' although never really supplanting power/cost ratio.

Then the accountant began probing the darker corners of the subject. How long would a machine last before it needed replacement? How often did it break down? What was the cost of repair? Reliability was the new fashion which threatens to be with us, not only in electric motors, but in electronic and mechanical equipment long into the next century. As more households acquire a food mixer, a washing machine, a spin drier, a tumble-air drier, a dishwasher, a vacuum cleaner, several hair driers (!), an electric carving knife, an electric razor, a TV, a portable TV, a video recorder, tape decks, record players, electric lawn mower and other electrical garden implements, reliability of all had better be high or a repair man of one skill or another will be visiting twice a week, to say nothing of plumbers, decorators, gas men and all the more traditionally necessary callers.

Along with reliability, there have come other new, generally rather less important fashions, which include absence of noise, absence of pollution, and safety.

Safety is a strange commodity. When we set up a national electricity supply, we fixed household voltages at 230–240 volts on the grounds that it would not kill *too* many people a year—four or five at most! In the USA they went for greater safety at 110 volts so as to kill no one—by accidentally touching a wire whilst standing on a carpeted floor, that is. (An electric fire tossed into a bath will kill the occupant with

110 volts just as effectively as will 230 volts!) In the grinding wheel industry safety regulations are so strict that not one death a year is allowed as the result of a burst wheel. But on the roads we slaughter each other by the thousand annually and this is regarded as 'kind of normal'. We are indeed a funny folk!

Fashion is a luxury that evolution never tried, or at least never tolerated—or I could be wrong; perhaps the dinosaurs could be said to constitute a fashion in reptiles?

BIG NAMES

Big Names in science are well known because they are taught in schools. Galileo, Newton, Einstein are household words. But try asking the man in the street who Bessemer was, or Lee de Forest or Osborne Reynolds or Miles Walker. Or simply ask, 'Who invented stainless steel?'

In considering the really big names one *must* be conscious of Newton's famous statement: 'If I have seen further it is by standing on the shoulders of giants.' This is the complete answer to the pessimists who will tell you that in electronics, or internal combustion engines, or electric motors, or any other subject: 'It has all been done.' If Newton drew his inspiration from those he considered greater than himself, and succeeded thereby, just think how many 'giants' are *now* available for us to stand upon in order to see further. The opportunities for inventing were never greater than they are *now*. This will remain true until the progress of engineering begins to slow—or rather, ceases to accelerate quite so fast! There are more engineers alive today than have ever died. These are the facts.

But giants are important, if only to show us how engineering diversified *because* of the giants, and thus to lead us to the next chapter on the many genera and species of engineer there are (to borrow biological terms). Actually this is a very good analogy, for from such considerations come the ideas of hybrids, sub-species and the biological concepts, although it should be said at once and with emphasis that whilst a biological hybrid is invariably infertile, hybrid engineers are often the most fertile of all when it comes to ideas, new products and a bold approach to the subject.

A BIT MORE HISTORY

Occasionally we can look back at a man centuries before his time, whose work is only recognised by others when they have trod a similar path. Such a man was Hero, about whom so little is known that his birth is given only approximately as AD 20, and his lifespan is anyone's guess. In assessing the importance of Hero's work, it is well to remember that he lived in Greece just after the great days of Greek science were over. Hero was without doubt an engineer; he used an engineer's methods. His most famous invention was that of a hollow metal sphere to which two bent tubes were attached. When he boiled water inside the sphere the steam emerged with force from the tubes and spun the sphere. Without doubt he produced the world's first steam turbine, before the reciprocating steam engine which is generally supposed to have come first and before Newton produced his law of 'action and reaction' (which incidentally was stated clearly by Leonardo da Vinci much earlier). Hero also described the basic machines: the lever, the pulley and the inclined plane. He constructed siphons, syringes, gear wheels and screw threads. He also wrote a book on light, declaring it to travel at infinite speed. He got the law of reflection absolutely correct.

When a man is so far ahead of his time his work has to wait for others to re-discover it, or for some other facet of human society to create the need for it. Generally, the latter comes first, but not in Hero's case. Having established the principle of steam power it was put to use to open doors, rotate statues and propel children's toys. This is hardly surprising, since it represented just about all the peaceful technology that existed at the time.

As Asimov remarks in his *Biographical Encyclopedia of Science and Technology*:

The idea of utilising the energy implicit in inanimate nature as a substitute for strained and aching slave muscle seemed to occur to no one. The idea was not to arise for seventeen centuries after Hero and then only in regions where slave labor did not exist and non-slave labor was getting more expensive.

'The unconscious accountant'—we might almost comment.

From such ideas came the expression 'Necessity is the mother of invention' but this, as you see, was quite wrong in the case of Hero, and indeed the same applies to most inventions. *Curiosity* is the mother of invention and never, in engineering, ever forget it. The best things are always done in the spirit of: 'I wonder what would happen if I did this.' It has been said that engineers are therefore children, but again it should be put the other way around. We are all born engineers to explore the fascinating universe in which we have arrived, and babies go to work on exploration as soon as their component parts work—mouths first, then arms, then legs. See the delight on a baby's face when it first pushes an object off a pram cover and sees the effect of gravity—soon whole bags of apples or tomatoes go one by one to the floor! The engineer is awake and aroused, intrigued and full of curiosity. What might we do if we maintained the pressures at that level all our lives? Parents have a lot to answer for!

But the school teacher has more. For the naturally curious child is directed into pure science in which, according to modern legend, all the imagination and curiosity is needed— to invent new particles, new theories, to search for the origin of the universe (quite ignoring the fact that it might not have had one). The engineer is supposed to be the jackal that feeds on the scraps thrown to him by the 'lion' scientist, to make what profit out of it he can.

When, all the time, almost the reverse is true. Engineers need the curiosity and the ingenuity to overcome real problems, with real objects in a real society, to invent new devices, new substances and new processes that will make life easier and better for their fellow humans. One needs no better example of this than in the plastics industry. I well remember in my sixth-form school-days being shown the first piece of transparent plastic I had ever seen, by my physics master, who was marvelling at the fact that it would drill as easily as wood, would take a screw thread like a metal, and behave optically like glass, without the danger of cuts from smashed pieces. The popular press forecast that within twenty years plastics would have revolutionised the appearance of most of our kitchens at home. No one believed them. It was just 'newspaper talk'. But it all happened, even sooner than predicted. What proportion of the people who did it were scientists and what engineers? The likely figures, if they could ever be sifted, would certainly be biased at least 95% to 5% in favour of the engineers. Engineers see the possibility of discoveries. Scientists are often content just to demonstrate a principle.

Although the next historical Big Name is somewhat out of dated order I take it now, since it illustrates precisely the point I have just made. The Name is Nikola Tesla and the time is the 1870s. The subject is electric motors. Tesla knew that whilst only *direct* current motors existed for all industrial drives, *alternating* current was obviously best for transmitting power, via transformers, so that the voltage could be stepped up to avoid high losses in the transmission lines (high voltage means low current for the same amount of power). Tesla reckoned that it ought to be possible to utilise a.c. directly in a motor that had no electrical connections to the moving part. Such a motor, he declared, would 'dominate the world of electric drives'. It was a tremendously ambitious dream. He had only the d.c. motor to look at for ideas and inspiration; a.c. was basically single phase. When once he realised that rotation of a conducting object in a pulsating magnetic field would produce a rotating component within that same field, he made his first breakthrough. But to expect such a rotating field, generated as it was by the rotation, to produce a twisting force on its creator *in the same direction* as the existing motion was asking for perpetual motion, surely? If not that, then the system was at least analogous to someone pulling himself into the air by heaving upwards on his own boot laces!

By 1882 Tesla had worked on the theory and shown that such acceleration forces were possible. But he had made one error. He had argued that the rotating field had to be 100% pure, with no pulsating component left, and that this situation was only attainable when the rotor was running in exact synchronism with the field, at which point it could, by definition, produce no torque. In 1882 he wrote in his notes that what he sought was impossible. He was very poor. He dug roads to make a living.

But the strength of the man was such that despite his mathematical proof that the brushless a.c. motor was impossible, *he went on looking for it!* Note that even had he had a modern computer it would have been of no help, for he would have fed it the equations which led to the answer—'Impossible'.

For six years he wrestled with the problem and in 1888, at a single stroke, he perfected it. Commercial machines were being built and used within a few years. But note the dates carefully. Whilst his battle with impossibility was going on in the USA, an English professor of physics named Baily gave a lecture in London in 1879 on electricity, during which he showed a number of demonstrations, one of which was clearly a two-phase induction motor with a capacitor feeding the second set of coils to split the phase. But it was the schoolbook, 'bottle-cork and knitting-needle' rotor type of motor and, having demonstrated it, he pushed it aside declaring that it would have no commercial value! In a recent lecture I likened Baily to a child who was coming home from school and saw a diamond on the ground, picked it up because it shone, lost it on the way home and never knew what it was worth. Tesla's invention went on to dominate the world of electric drives as he had predicted, and today over 95% of the total power of all electric motors in the world is supplied by induction motors.

CHRONOLOGICAL ORDER

Unlike political or international history, the history of engineering can almost be written by someone who knows nothing but the products of technology and has a superficial knowledge of what manufactured articles came before. For example, you could not have internal combustion engines before you had invented hard steel. So Bessemer's invention of 1856 was a true landmark of progress, after which many things were possible. We might note, in passing, that the direct pressure to make such a steel came, as such things often do, from the evils of war. Bessemer's earlier invention was that of making bullets spin in order to help them maintain a straight flight. The inspiration for this came from the Crimean War. He hoped to apply the same principle to cannon shells. History records that the conservative British War Office was not interested, so Bessemer went to Britain's ally, France, and found Napoleon III was interested. But to achieve spin, the projectile would have to fit so tightly in the barrel that, as a French artillery expert derisively pointed out, the excess pressure thus created would almost certainly explode the weapon and annihilate the gunners without harming the enemy.

Stung into action by this quite just criticism, Bessemer set himself the task of making a form of iron that would be strong enough for the cannon, and came up with the process of adding oxygen to burn off the unwanted carbon in the steel by a direct blast of air. The blast furnace was born and it had the added bonus of producing steel at a fraction of its previous cost.

The results were to be seen in giant ocean liners, steel-skeletoned skyscrapers and huge suspension bridges. The order of these developments is obviously predictable without knowing any of the Big Names.

On the lighter side of engineering, a similar order of events occurred, each new technology apparently awaiting the arrival of a Big Name before the leap forward could be achieved. In 1822 Charles Babbage planned a highly complex and elaborate computer, but it was all to be made from electrical relays which were slow to operate and his big machine was never completed. He was, of course, waiting for the invention of the triode valve by Lee de Forest (another Big Name) in 1906. You will invariably find that the Big Names invented many things other than those for which they are

NOTE Ⓐ Ⓑ

eventually remembered. We have already seen that Bessemer invented the rifle with its spinning bullet. Babbage had a big influence on the introduction of the 'penny post' in 1840; he worked out the first reliable actuarial tables (now the insurance company's 'bread and butter'). He invented the first speedometer, skeleton keys and the locomotive 'cow-catcher' which became popular in North America. One cannot fail to note also the wide variety of products that flow from the brain of one engineer, illustrating perhaps above all else his versatility and freedom of thought, unfettered by laws of physics or by who says this or that 'can't be done'. Babbage went on to invent the ophthalmoscope, even though it is always credited to Helmholtz. (This, because Babbage 'forgot about it' for four years!)

Ⓐ

Lee de Forest worked out a glow lamp which could convert the irregularities of sound waves into electric currents which would therefore affect the brightness of a lamp. This could be photographed along with a motion picture. In 1923 he demonstrated the first sound motion picture (the 'talkies').

FIREBOX
DIAPHRAM

LOOK, HERE I AM, ALL THE TIME!

What is also interesting in engineering discovery particularly is that so often a key invention is staring us in the face, often for centuries, simply waiting to be noticed! Whilst Lee de Forest's triode was founding the electronics industry in the 1920s and the Golden Way seemed to be to ask questions such as: If a third electrode (the grid) in a vacuum valve will extend its use from mere rectification to amplification, what might another electrode do?—the tetrode—splendid! Then what about a fifth—the pentode—better still! And with this now antiquated and clumsy piece of technology the world's first big Universal Computers were built in the 1950s. Babbage was apparently waiting for the pentode.

Ⓑ

And yet whilst all of Lee de Forest's pioneering work that made it possible was going on in the 1920s, amateur radio enthusiasts on both sides of the Atlantic were using a 'cat's whisker' (a thin wire) to 'tickle' an impure crystal containing some germanium and making the necessary rectifier. Not exactly regarded as 'cranks', they were put aside as those who practised an art (almost a 'black art'!). The 'tickling' process, as we now know, was the means of trying to put the sharp end of the thin wire into contact with a particularly favourable bit of crystal. Again the world waited for another Big Name, and it came in the form of William Shockley, who first discovered that the secret of the crystal and cat's whisker lay in the *purity* of the germanium. The year was 1948 (the first valve computer was 1951). The 'transistor' that resulted miniaturised practically every piece of electronics on the market. Electronics was almost a new subject. As befits a Big Name, Shockley had earlier been associated with Bozorth, Dillinger, Williams and others in expounding the domain theory of magnets which led to a whole new range of magnetic materials.

But if new engineering principles and devices are often found to exist in raw materials and other inanimate objects, simply waiting, often virtually screaming, to be noticed, how much more true must it be of living creatures who could be said to have been practising engineering for over 800 million years, compared with our mere 30,000. I believe that there is to be seen, in nature, all the exploitation of engineering principles that mankind has ever used, and thousands more of which we are not even aware. So much so, that I have devoted a whole chapter to this aspect (chapter 6), in the hope both of encouraging schools to make it possible to study biology in the sixth form, as well as the 'usual three'—maths, physics, chemistry—and of bringing into the engineering profession mature students with a first degree in biology.

3

Sub-species of Engineer

'Variety's the very spice of life'. (*William Cowper*)

There are as many ways of classifying engineers as there are of arranging butterflies in a collection. In the latter case you may elect to put all those of one *size* in the same case, or you may decide to separate them into basic colours, 'yellows' in one case, 'blues' in another. Most people, I think, would want to keep moths separate from butterflies, although there is no need to do this. Some species of one group bear almost all the characteristics of the other. The more precise among us would want to keep the separate families or 'genera' together. Others will want to arrange a case on purely 'artistic' grounds with a complete mixture.

In engineering, it would be possible to divide engineers into those that deal principally with the properties of water, those that deal with the earth and those that deal with the atmosphere. But this is a very broad classification. Under 'water' would appear marine engineers who range all the way from those who build cranes for docks to those who plan future cities under the sea (an exciting concept now rapidly transferring itself from the realms of science fiction to those of reality). There would be shipbuilders and maintainers for all kinds of vessels including hovering craft and hydrofoils, these

27

last two clearly overlapping the skills of those whose natural medium is the air.

In the 'land' engineers would be included those who mine minerals and refine them, metallurgists, mineralogists and geologists. Then there are those who mould the land, the road and rail builders, the designers and makers of power stations, and the bridge and tower builders. One of the more 'exotic' projects in this group is the recently constructed 'power station inside a mountain' at Dinorwic in North Wales, where a small lake on top of a small mountain is emptied each day down a 10 metre diameter stainless steel pipe threaded through from the mountain top to drive water wheel generators right in the heart of the mountain, after which it fills up a lake at the foot of the mount. At night, when the demand for electricity is low, the water is pumped back to the top again. This enables the power station plant to even out its load between night and day and then run the machinery much more efficiently.

Those who exploit the air build aircraft and helicopters, balloons and rockets. But they also research the possibilities of harnessing the wind to produce energy for our use. They explore the possibilities of trying to control the weather, even though the results may be only on a small scale. There are chemical engineers who concern themselves with the pollution of the atmosphere.

A fourth group could be said to concentrate on the sun and to engineer methods of capturing the maximum amount of energy from it by the most direct means—solar panels. There are clearly other groups in such a classification for none so far mentioned has been concerned with engineering in medicine, in the hospital, nor with food manufacture nor with that vast range of products described under the modern blanket words 'consumer goods'.

A DIFFERENT CLASSIFICATION

Let us therefore seek a different classification in which we come nearer to describing the kind of work that the engineers do. For example we may begin with the planners. Master planners advise ministers in government on the siting of new airports, or docks, or the closing of railway lines, or the building of new ring roads around cities, or the planning of cities themselves. These people hardly ever do any *real* engineering. They meet in committees most of their working time and talk *all* of the time. They seldom use a tool, or even choose a material, though they may on occasions get as far as arguing the colour of the paint! They advise governments, local authorities, occasionally individuals, as to which firms should get the contracts to *do* the jobs. This brings us to the second class of engineer, dividing them in this way, namely those who sit in management of large firms. They also sit on committees a great deal and talk most of the time. They consult accountants, watch the stock market, their competitors, the cost of living and the current trends, which I have labelled 'fashion'. Some of this class are concerned with personal relations with the staff and the workers. Some are concerned with sales and with advertising, but only as far as making sure that they never get bogged down in the detail of either topic, or for that matter, any of the other topics I have listed.

Working down the list we now reach those whom the planners consult. They too largely sit in offices, sometimes on committees, they also talk a lot both 'upwards' and 'downwards'—upwards to senior management and downwards to project leaders, heads of departments such as research, education and training. They occasionally go and look at things being made, either indoors or outdoors, depending on what products their companies are concerned with. They may travel abroad a great deal, or not at all. Again it depends on the company and the nature of its business.

Next come what I would call the do-ers. These engineers are the backbone of the industry. They have the responsibility of overseeing design, co-ordinating manufacture with promised delivery dates (in the case of manufactured articles). They pick the teams to do the jobs, pat some on the back, fire others! Naturally they talk a lot too, but they occasionally do calculations (more on pocket calculators than on computers—

they have 'slaves' to use the computers). Sometimes they get involved in the actual work itself (like going down a mine, or on to an oil rig). This class includes the people who actually do the selling and produce the publicity, the leaflets, the TV adverts and so on. But please remember that although this classification is to some extent concerned with rank, length of service, etc., not all those within the group are paid comparable salaries, by any means!

The next 'layer' in this classification are more concerned with the *detailed* design of one product, or component of a product. They may be concerned with commissioning a new plant, or with what is known as 'trouble-shooting' on existing plant. They will use tools as well as computers. They will make more direct use of the theory they learned at university in their everyday lives than will those in the higher strata. As such, they may tend to feel superior to their elders rather in the manner in which the 'Gammas' looked down on the 'Betas' in Aldous Huxley's *Brave New World*. But they are all Chartered Engineers. They have all been through the educational mill, the training mill and the 'responsibility' phase. They are fully fledged engineers of all kinds and with a truly bewildering range of jobs, which brings us to our next method of classification.

EVOLUTIONARY CLASSIFICATION

This method is much more like a biological classification coupled with an evolutionary process which is constantly producing new species (and making a few extinct, though not to the same extent that nature does). This classification largely follows the narrative of the previous chapter, for example in the beginning were the Big Three

civil
mechanical } engineers
electrical

soon to be joined by the fourth giant, the aeronautical engineers. Here social history plays its part and where there are towns and cities there are municipal engineers. Then there are the structural engineers and the metallurgists and the mining engineers and those concerned with mineralogy, petrology, geology and the like, all of which could claim to have older roots than those of the aeronautical engineers. Chemical engineers are a 'natural' in this classification and their daily routines are very different from those of chemists. In the more modern world there are production engineers, oil engineers, textile and paper-making engineers. This is the classification that most nearly brings out the 'species' of engineer in the analogous way that species of plant or mammal or fish emerged. So like their biological counterparts there are bound to be sub-species and one does not have to look far to see these in a profession such as electrical engineering.

From the 'type' species of 'electrical', that I am old enough to claim to have been, when a three-year undergraduate course could teach you most facets of the subject, it divided into, first, heavy current (machines and power systems) and light current (electronics and communications). Then there came others that bridged the disciplines, like control engineering which is clearly not limited to electricals, and this of course is where the hybridisation began. But even as I write, control engineering is having to accept new sub-species, such as robotics, just as electronics gave rise to a branch known as computer engineering, which soon split itself into hardware and software.

A UNIVERSITY CLASSIFICATION

One of the ways of elaborating on this list of 'species' and 'sub-species' given in the previous section is to go through the calendar of a large university science and technology section, and list the various topics of engineering, many of which carry a Chair in what might be described as one of the species or sub-species of the professions. Let us begin with my own establishment of Imperial College, labelling each topic as a species, sub-species, or in some cases a hybrid.

31

When there is a Chair in a subject it generally means that there is a supporting staff and that active research is going on there. There are also likely to be at least optional lectures that undergraduates may attend, for university courses tend to be extremely flexible, a direct result in fact of there being so many different disciplines (species and sub-species) in engineering. First-year courses tend to be fairly rigid. This is necessary to make the bridge between schoolwork, which may have had little engineering content for most, and university work, which would have been different, even had it been a continuation of physics or maths or chemistry. As the undergraduate progresses from first to final year, there is more and more opportunity for choice until, by final year, one hopes that the students are attending courses that they are really crazy about, for the thirst for knowledge inevitably brings its own reward in the examination results.

Though not directly connected with classification a slight digression here is perhaps permissible, having now drifted into my own profession of university teaching.

Each year I see hundreds of first-year engineers starting their university courses, each determined to do well, as they should. For acceptance at a university is virtually an admission (although of course, no one will ever admit to it officially) that you are capable of at least a lower 2nd class Honours degree. Yet we know that a small percentage will fall from grace and either fail or give up the struggle before the end. Somehow they lose the 'spark', and I can do no better in trying to define the spark than to tell you a true story of a local grocer's son, well known to me many years ago.

His school record was abysmal. But he collected British moths and whenever I went in the shop on my way home from work (the shop was kept open late) his mother, who served in the shop, was instructed to give him a call and he would come and show me the interesting species he had caught since he last saw me (I, of course, am a collector, too!) One night I called at the shop when he was out. His mother said ruefully: 'I don't know *what* we're going to do with Richard. He's bottom of his class again.' Then she added angrily: 'Do you know, that lad knows the Latin names of all the British moths by heart.' By this she meant the classical generic and specific names of each, and as there are some 900 species of British moth, not counting the Microlepidoptera (mostly very tiny species) this amounted to 1800 not very memorable and in some cases not even very pronounceable names, each to be associated with a visible animal, many of which resemble each other very closely.

'Well,' I replied to the worried mother, 'the explanation is very simple. He *wants to know* the names of the moths. If only he wanted to know about the countries of the world instead, he would be top of his class in geography. Or if they had a school subject on moth classification, he would be top in that too.' So the message for young engineers is clear. Be sure you *want* to do the subjects you select in Finals, and are not doing them because they seem to be 'fashionable' among your colleagues nor because they seem to offer the best job opportunities. If you choose what you want to know about, and get a 'First', you will have no difficulty in manipulating yourself into a well-paid job. 'Wanting to know' is *all there is* in education.

To return to the university classification theme, here is the most up-to-date calendar list for Imperial College.

AERONAUTICAL ENGINEERING	Species
Aeronautical structures	Sub-species
Experimental aerodynamics	Sub-species
Physiological flow studies	Hybrid
BIO-TECHNOLOGY	New species or new hybrid
CHEMICAL ENGINEERING	Species
Applied catalysis	Sub-species
Combustion	Hybrid
Interface science	Hybrid
Mechanics and thermophysics of fluids	Sub-species
Nuclear technology	Hybrid
Properties of matter	Sub-species
Transfer processes	Sub-species

CIVIL ENGINEERING	Super-species
Concrete structures and technology	Sub-species
Engineering seismology	Sub-species, could become species
Hydraulics	Species
Public health and water resource engineering	Sub-species
Soil mechanics	Species
Structural engineering	Species
Surveying	Sub-species
Systems and mechanics	Hybrid
Timber structures and technology	Sub-species and possible biological hybrid
Transport	Sub-species, becoming species
COMPUTING	Species
Communications	Sub-species
Computational logic	Sub-species
Computing science	Sub-species
Graphics	Sub-species
Microprocessors	Sub-species
Programming methodology	Sub-species
ELECTRICAL ENGINEERING	Super-species
Computer-aided design	Sub-species
Control systems	Sub-species
Digital communications	Sub-species
Electrical materials	Sub-species/hybrid
Electromagnetic fields	Sub-species
Engineering in medicine	Hybrid
Information engineering	New sub-species
Machines	Sub-species
Microelectronic applications	Sub-species
Optical systems and devices	Sub-species
Power systems	Sub-species
Robotics, special drives, power electronics	New sub-species/hybrid
Signal processing	Sub-species
Solid state electronics	Sub-species

ENVIRONMENTAL TECHNOLOGY	New species
GEOLOGY	Species
Crystallography and mineralogy	Sub-species
Engineering geology	Sub-species
Flow in rock	Sub-species
Geochemistry	Hybrid
Geophysics	Hybrid
Minerals engineering and technology	Sub-species
Mining geology	Sub-species
Ore geology and mineralogy	Sub-species
Palaeontology	Sub-species
Petroleum geology	Sub-species
Sedimentology	Sub-species
Stratigraphy	Sub-species
Structural geology	Sub-species
HISTORY OF TECHNOLOGY	Species
MARINE TECHNOLOGY	Species
MECHANICAL ENGINEERING	Super-species
Applied mechanics	Sub-species
Biomechanics	Hybrid
Dynamics	Sub-species
Elasticity and plasticity	Sub-species
Fluid mechanics, heat transfer and combustion	Sub-species
Gas turbine technology	Sub-species
Industrial metal forming	Sub-species
Internal combustion engines	Sub-species
Manufacturing technology	Sub-species
Nuclear power	Hybrid
Polymer engineering	Could be a new species
Properties of materials	Sub-species
Robotics	Hybrid
Statics	Sub-species
Strength of materials	Sub-species
Stress analysis	Sub-species
Thermal power engineering	Sub-species
Thermodynamics	Sub-species
Total technology	New species

Tribology	Sub-species
Vibration analysis	Sub-species
METALLURGY AND MATERIALS SCIENCE	Species
Aqueous systems	Sub-species
Casting, welding and heat treatment	Sub-species
Chemistry of materials production	Hybrid
Corrosion and degradation	Sub-species
Electronic structure and properties	Hybrid
Hydrometallurgy	Sub-species
Materials stability and process principles	Sub-species
Mechanical working and powder metallurgy	Sub-species
Metal production	Sub-species
Microstructure and properties	Sub-species
Process engineering	Sub-species
Performance of materials	Sub-species
Pyrometallurgy	Sub-species
Solid state chemistry	Hybrid
Structure and properties of non-metallic materials	Sub-species
Technology of discrete electrical devices	Hybrid
Technology of semiconductor devices	Hybrid
MINERAL RESOURCES ENGINEERING	Species
Drilling and production engineering	Sub-species
Mineral technology	Hybrid
Mining	Sub-species
Mining—rock fragmentation	Sub-sub-species
Mining—transportation	Sub-sub-species
Mining—ventilation	Sub-sub-species
Petroleum engineering	Hybrid
Reservoir engineering	Sub-species
Rock mechanics	Sub-species
ROBOTICS AND AUTOMATED SYSTEMS	New sub-species

From other universities' calendars it is possible to compile a further list of topics in subjects not listed at Imperial College, but all in British universities. Just a few samples are quoted here:

Aeronautical and astronautical engineering	New species
Production technology and management	Species
Safety and hygiene	Species
Food technology	Species/hybrid
Dairy technology	Sub-species
Poultry technology	Sub-species
Agricultural communication	Sub-species
Space research	Hybrid
Colour technology	Sub-species
Design of manufacturing systems	Sub-species
Textile design and structure	Species
Industrial management	Species
Marketing	Sub-species
Organisational analysis	Sub-species
Industrial relations	Sub-species
Industrial aerodynamics	Sub-species
Building technology	Species
Cybernetics	Species
High-voltage engineering	Sub-species
Theoretical gas dynamics	Sub-species
Automobile engineering	Almost a species
Vehicle design	Sub-species
Design of machine systems	Sub-species
Precision engineering	Sub-species
Materials handling	Sub-species

The list could continue for many pages.

We must conclude that this kind of classification has the one merit of causing the reader to exclaim, as is supposed to be the case in the television advertisement for *TV Times*, 'I never knew there was so much in it!'

Otherwise long lists of topics can be both boring and confusing and convince the school-leaver that he or she now *certainly* has no idea what they want to do. 'Better stick to physics, I suppose.'—No, don't! There is just as long and confusing diversification of effort in the pure sciences and most of them are not as much *fun* as are the engineering ones. Besides, the above lists are not by any means the 'end of the line'. I need only mention, perhaps, one single example to illustrate the interplay between departments which allows you to deflect yourself from one specialised line to another, as you progress towards final year at university. It is this:

The Aeronautics Department at Imperial College has an 'animal laboratory'!

TAKEN FOR GRANTED

There are obviously other classifications one could make. For example, by main occupation. Engineers may

plan, design, test, maintain, trouble-shoot, organise manu-facture, organise production, sell, advertise, teach, research,

and so on, and each of these applies in all of the various disciplines I have just outlined by means of university departments. Even before that, the main theme can be subdivided. For example those who plan may do so on behalf of next year's sales, taking into account new products, or they may do market research, which roughly means finding out what the competitors are making and what they are charging for it. The planners may be almost wholly concerned with finance—whether to put up new buildings and invest in new plant or to shut down a non-profitable line. When a famous chocolate firm decided to introduce a new candy bar, the production line to make them cost three-quarters of a million pounds. Think of the engineering content of such a venture. Think of the engineering that has gone into almost every article in every one of your rooms at home or at school.

Surely engineering is the one profession above all others that we need most and notice least. We simply take it for granted that the ships that bring our food will not sink. We take it for granted that the wineglasses at our dinner party will not suddenly shatter through internal stress. In fact, we take nearly all of it for granted.

What perhaps is interesting are the things that we do *not* take for granted. These include

> The car will start in the mornings.
> The television set will not break down.
> The trains will run to time.
> The aeroplane that takes us on holiday will not develop a fault.

If our fears for the first two are well-founded, it is not national news. If either of the second pair becomes serious, it is inclined to be reported through the media. Notice how only the last has anything in common with the medical profession in that it involves personal safety. In all four there is a large area of 'no–man's land' where prediction is of no help. In only the last two is there always a chance of apportioning blame. The human element is ever-present. With the first two it is accepted almost philosophically that 'things wear out', and therefore that kind of mishap is inevitable. But consider rather how many engineering things 'go right' in the course of a day, and how many people earn their living in making sure that that situation obtains. The pistons in a 6-cylinder family car doing 70 mph on a motor-way move once up and down in a cylinder about 85 times every second. This means that in travelling 70 miles along that motorway, each piston has moved up and down a few inches 306,000 times, and the amount of wear has to be seen to be negligible! After 3000 miles it is usual to change the oil because it has become blackened by tiny particles of metal rubbed off the piston rings or cylinder walls, making the lubrication less efficient. This, note, is after each piston has made over 13 million excursions up and down the cylinder. Still that metal that turned the oil black must not have worn away enough metal to make the piston perform significantly worse, or it will need new piston rings or at worst, a re-bored cylinder. One looks for this kind of wear after about 100,000 miles or more, which amounts to 437 million strokes of the piston. What an engineering achievement to take for granted!

Again, in a journey from London to Edinburgh the average saloon car wheel revolves over a third of a million times, which means that each bit of rubber tyre hits the ground the same number of times, stretching and contracting at each contact. Think of the chemical engineering, the materials science and the mechanical engineering that have gone into making tyres that will take that and many other similar journeys in their stride.

There are equivalent 'near-miracles' all around us in the technological society in which we live today. A television picture in the UK contains 625 'lines', and the picture changes 25 times a second, so that in an hour's programme, the capacitors in the circuits of the line scan charge and discharge over 56 million times!

And we curse if one of them grows tired and burns out, because it invariably does it just at the start of *one* member of the family's favourite programme. Then the burning questions are only, *'Who* will put it right?' and 'How long will it take?' Those who 'maintain' are more important than those who design, for the average family. Nationally, those who sell are probably more important than those who teach.

I wrote this chapter on classification in the hope of alerting you not only to the immense variety and complexity of the job structure that lies before you in engineering. I have now tried to jolt you out of the idea that some of you may have whilst doing sixth-form mathematics and physics that 'ordinary' things *just happen*. They don't; they have to be *made* to happen. Indeed a way of describing the engineering profession, if not in 'words of one syllable', at least in very simple language, is to say that it is 'making things happen'. This of course is not to be used out of context. Imagine contestants in a TV panel game being introduced as: 'This is Miss Jones who is a secretary, next Mr Johnson who is a botanist, whilst Mr Brown makes things happen.' The mentality of the average viewer is now geared to assume that this *must* be a joke! But how better could you describe the flight engineer on a jumbo jet? He had better 'make things happen' or it will go ill for all of the passengers.

So please, never take us for granted. We *are* allied very closely to the tradespeople, the mechanic, the plumber, the electrician and the gas man. Somehow we never get *quite* as much limelight as either the tradespeople on the one hand, nor the 'glamour' people on the other, and these include the actors and actresses, racing-car drivers, boxers and all-in wrestlers, authors, politicians and surgeons. But we are no less dedicated. Our 'show must go on' because people rely on having electricity and water and gas, and a TV set and a toilet. And they take most of these for granted.

THE VITAL CLASSIFICATION

I have deliberately left out, so far, the most obvious classification of engineers (or of any other kind of person) and that is simply the three classes:

Good
Mediocre
Bad

Let me say at once that in any collection of people who have a particular skill, the *majority* are mediocre. This is the definition of mediocre. They are never to be thought of as bad, inferior, poor, inadequate or any similar derisory description. The last time engineers are likely to be categorised into these classes is in their first degree at university. There are no classifications for higher degrees, no percentages for engineering practice, subsequent to the education phase. If the customers rate what you do as low, they will go somewhere else in the future. This is the only indication you will have.

I tell my students that when I set their examination paper I have a method of sorting out the three categories which would not necessarily apply to other professions, and it is this.

I set 8 questions, of which they are required to answer only 5. Each question carries 20% of the marks, 40% is a pass. I promise to set 2 questions out of the 8 which are pure book-work—straight out of the lectures, and anyone who has been paying a reasonable amount of attention should get 20/20.

They may make a slip and get only 18 or 19. But the idea is to give everyone a chance to pass, *if they qualify as engineers.*

—And they qualify if they spot which *are* the 2 easy questions!

Then there are 2 more questions, usually in 2 parts each, the first part is again straightforward and allows the candidate to pick up another 8/20 for each, on the assumption of having attended the lectures and taken good notes. The other 12 marks per question will require some thought, over and above the usual regurgitation of bookwork, which is what school exams largely consist of, after all. So even if they only get a couple of 18/20's for the 2 easy questions, they stand a good chance of getting another 12 at least from these 2 middle-of-the-road questions, given them 48% and lifting them out of the 3rd class Honours trough.

But the other 4 questions are absolute swine! Only the best will get anywhere near these. Notice that I force every candidate to attempt at least *one* of these, for I do want to find out who is really good and worthy of 1st class Honours.

But woe betide the otherwise mediocre candidate who fails to spot which are the 4 swine and attempts all 4. Even if his or her 5th question is an 'easy', their marks are likely to be 19, 1, 0, 2, 3—total 25%—FAIL! I reckon they deserve to fail as engineers, because it is a prime requirement of every practising engineer that they know when they are 'up against it', i.e. when the problem is bigger than they are and they need help.

A phrase which should be well to the fore in the vocabulary of an engineer is, 'I don't know', but always followed by, 'but I will soon find out', or at least, 'but I will try to find out'. The process of finding out consists of either:

(1) Knowing a colleague who specialises in the topic in question.
(2) Knowing who the recognised authority in the topic is, even though you have never met, making an appointment officially, with or without money changing hands.
(3) Knowing how to use a technical library intelligently.
(4) Knowing that the problem *can* be solved, given the time and the necessary computer facilities.

In the medical profession there is a direct parallel. 'I should like a second opinion' can mean anything from 'I'm not absolutely sure' to a face-saving 'I haven't the vaguest idea what's wrong with you', or 'I've never seen anything like it before'. With people, of course, to admit the last of these would send the patients into sheer panic, but when a piece of machinery is the 'patient' there is no harm in declaring openly one's own limitations on the topic and bringing in the consultant, just as the medical practitioner does. Of course, if the consultant subsequently tells the customer that the engineer should have known and the problem was simple, the engineer has effectively just failed another examination!

But it is better that than to spend the odd half a million in the full belief that you know how to do it, when in fact you have embarked on an entirely wrong line of approach. This is why I maintain that the candidate who fails to spot the 4 'nasties' in the final examination paper fails as an engineer.

When you have had a lot of experience in the profession, you might wish to practise as a consultant. Academics in the engineering profession practise it frequently as a sideline and a second source of income, and because they are engaged in original research virtually from graduation, it is not uncommon for academically minded engineers of 22/23 years old to be earning money from consulting. There are whole firms that do nothing else but sort out other people's problems. There are far more consultants in the engineering profession than there are in the medical. Whether this is because the average medical practitioner is less willing than is the engineer to say 'I don't know', or whether it takes a lot more experience and skill to be a medical consultant, I know not. All I know is that the human machine is a far more complex structure than anything that men have built so far, so the number of 'I don't know's' ought to be greater!

4

Physics and Engineering

'Scientists explore what is; engineers create what has never been.'

(*Dr Theodore von Karman, American engineer*)

I am sometimes asked what kind of qualities an engineer needs in his or her make-up. Since it is the main object of this book to answer just that question it might seem stupid to try to give a single-sentence answer to the question at once, but I feel bound to try. An engineer must be able to cope with a new situation where no one else knows what to do and is looking to him/her with the kind of look that says: 'Well, you're a qualified engineer—get on with it!'—and you know that you must do something, rather than nothing, and that it had better be seen to be good!

When engineering science was first introduced into schools in the UK in the 1960s in lieu of physics it was a pleasant surprise to see just how many of the professors of physics at universities would accept it as a qualifying subject at 'A' level. The reason, of course, was that they saw that it *was* still physics, but written from an engineering point of view in which the reason for doing it was more obvious than perhaps it is in a more pure science.

This was especially well brought out by some of the early school-books on the subject. For example, a book on mechanics began on page 1 with a photograph of astronauts boarding a spaceship. Pages 2 to 15 dealt with problems of getting off the earth, of maintaining orbits around both earth and moon and of landing on the moon. If was page 16, rather than page 1, that carried a paragraph headed 'Mass'.

By now the reader did not have to be told the importance of mass nor even to have it 'defined' by that most unscientific of all definitions:

'Mass is the amount of matter in a body',

in which neither 'amount' nor 'matter' are truly defined and a little thought will show that in such a context, the word 'amount' has no meaning!

Similarly the build-up towards the inclined plane included a photograph of a yacht in full sail and the text talked about the importance of a keel. Now, of course, this was the way it occurred historically. Engineering made it necessary to measure things and accuracy became important. Measurement and accuracy could be said to make the dawn of science proper, although it was a long dawn.

With the modern advances in physics the search for the more and more *fundamental* bit of matter and the most remote part of the universe goes on relentlessly. But there are many practical jobs to be done that do not require such depth of insight into the physical world to arrive at a solution, even though the problems that they present are by no means less demanding than are those that occupy dedicated pure scientists.

ANALOGY

Perhaps my own branch of the subject, electrical engineering, may be regarded as being nearest to pure science, dealing as it does largely in intangible things such as electric current, voltage, charge and radiation. Yet even the electrical engineer is prepared to regard the electron as a little blob. His atom of hydrogen is an orange in London and a pinhead in Guildford orbiting it at about 25 miles radius. It will take him most of the way he will ever need to go in solving his problems and when it fails because it was not true, he will *know* it was not true and will seek advice from his physicist colleagues. For the orange/pinhead model is an example of the use of *analogy* and analogy is another name for a fairy story. Like a fairy story it is never true, but then it also points out a moral which can be all-rewarding. For an engineer his staple diet is analogy. He uses it in all he does, never ever being deluded about it being the *truth* or any such rubbish. The engineer begins perhaps by believing that there is no truth and that therefore those who seek it waste their time. But then engineers deal in compromise as a master art.

They must! The real world is not made of 'smooth light inextensible rods' as are the structures in 'A' level physics. What a world it would be if there were no friction. All cars and other machinery would at once fall to pieces as all nuts left their bolts! None of us would be able to propel ourselves along, except by an elaborate process of blowing and sucking air. The world of 'A' level physics is as remote from reality as a garden gnome is from a living creature. But in analogy, there is at least a pretence of an understanding and we use it when no other form of understanding exists.

Take electricity for example. I have never heard any teacher introduce the topic of electric current without using the idea of water flowing in a pipe. Teachers there may be who can; all I can say is that I would not want to have been one of their pupils. The great thing about the water analogy is that it gives at once a meaning and a concept of voltage. It is electrical pressure, the thing that drives current, and the student can go along convinced that the chain of understanding remains unbroken, even though there never was an understanding of the electric current at all, because there never was an explanation for 'charge'. Charge is one of the mystic quantities about which one can only say, 'If you have two of them they repel each other.' So magnetic pole is another, and strangest of all, SO IS MASS! Now to tell a physicist that mass is a mystic, inexplicable quantity is an anathema. But it was the line adopted by Faraday (whom I always regard as the father of engineering) and by Maxwell, who was to some extent Faraday's pupil by correspondence, for at the age of 21 Maxwell wrote on a clean page in his diary, 'The fundamental quantities of the universe are length, time and force', which sentiment is also to be found in Faraday's writings. Since that time, however, scientists have stuck to mass, rather than force, as the third fundamental dimension. Yet when the engineer of today examines the distinction it is at once clear that length, time and force are all things that a human can *experience*. Mass, is not.

[Now why should this be important to an engineer anyway? The answer is that the physicist never *did* get himself sorted out over mass. In particular, it has taken until the 1970s for any school physics book that I have ever seen to point out that there might even be a distinction between gravitational mass and inertial mass.

Nelkon and Parker's *Advanced Level Physics* (1977) points out clearly that when using mass in the force equation $F = $ mass $\times$ acceleration, it is 'inertial mass' that is being considered and they give it the symbol m. They define 'gravitational mass' as used in Newton's theory of attraction and give it the symbol m_g. They then work an example for the period of a simple pendulum and end with the glorious sentence: 'Experiments show that to a high degree of accuracy, $T = 2\pi\sqrt{l/g}$ no matter what mass is used, that is, the period depends only on l and g. Thus $m = m_g$, or the gravitational mass is equal to the inertial mass to the best of our present knowledge.' Those last seven words should be printed in pure gold!

I will go further and prove that the two forms of mass do not even have the same *dimension*.

In old-fashioned physics, before the introduction of SI units, it was customary to work out dimensional analysis as two separate systems. These were known as 'electrostatic' and 'electromagnetic' and were derived as shown in Table 4.1. It is obvious (or should be) that you are going to get precisely the same form of answer for $[m]$ as for $[q]$ because the starting equations are identical except that the letters are different and mean different things. Notice also how the techniques are identical in that in each case it is the dimensions of the mystic quantity that are sought and the student is told that neither q nor m can be resolved *absolutely* because there are no known dimensions for μ or ε. The introduction of SI units dug a hole

Table 4.1

	Electrostatic	Electromagnetic
Basic equation	$F = \dfrac{q_1 q_2}{\varepsilon d^2}$	$F = \dfrac{m_1 m_2}{\mu d^2}$
'Mystic' quantity	q (charge)	m (magnetic pole)
Extra quantity of unknown dimensions	ε (permittivity)	μ (permeability)
Analysis in terms of M, L, T	$[MLT^{-2}] = \dfrac{q^2}{\varepsilon L^2}$	$[MLT^{-2}] = \dfrac{m^2}{\mu L^2}$
Hence:	$[q] = [\varepsilon^{\frac{1}{2}} M^{\frac{1}{2}} L^{\frac{3}{2}} T^{-1}]$	$[m] = [\mu^{\frac{1}{2}} M^{\frac{1}{2}} L^{\frac{3}{2}} T^{-1}]$

for this ignorance and buried it deep, declaring with authority that ε had the dimensions of farads/metre whilst μ was of dimension henrys/metre, never stopping to answer the question, 'What is a henry?' because the answer was too embarrassing. A henry is a μ-metre! Who is pulling the wool over whose eyes? If a thing is inexplicable, who is going to be able to explain it simply by changing the units?

Now we move on to mass and obtain a third starting equation of identical form to the first two, viz.

$$F = \frac{G\, M_1\, M_2}{d^2}$$

except that Isaac chose to put his constant on top of the fraction. To make it identical therefore, we can write it as

$$F = \frac{M_1\, M_2}{(1/G)d^2}$$

Proceeding as before we should surely get:

$$[MLT^{-2}] = \left[\frac{M_g{}^2}{(1/G)d^2}\right]$$

using Nelkon and Parker's distinction between inertial mass M and gravitational mass M_g. The answer will of course be identical in form to the other two

$$[M_g] = [G^{-\frac{1}{2}} M^{\frac{1}{2}} L^{\frac{3}{2}} T^{-1}]$$

but you will never find this in any respectable physics book. What you *will* find is:

$$[MLT^{-2}] = \frac{G M^2}{d^2}$$

Hence $$[G] = [M^{-1} L^3 T^{-2}] \qquad (4.1)$$

The mystic quantity has disappeared and we have succeeded in effectively finding absolute dimensions for the quantity comparable to ε and μ. There is only one suitable comment for this equation (4.1)—'It is rubbish!' It is the result of cancelling M with M_g. It suggests that you get a *different* answer by starting with identical equations and pretending to give each identical treatments.]

An alternative way of expressing the difference in approach between physics and engineering is by way of equations. In fifth forms one learns to solve pairs of simultaneous equations where there are 2 unknowns and 2 equations. In sixth forms the 2 is extended to n unknowns and equations and one learns about an organised approach through determinants and matrices. In physics research there may even be 19 unknowns and only 17 equations with certain other, rather vague, guiding constraints. With the aid of computers one learns such techniques as 'hill climbing' where it is possible to obtain a unique optimum answer even though there are one or two more unknowns than equations. But the poor engineer is invariably faced with a 21-equations–89-unknowns situation. What is more, nothing is going to tell him which 21 of the 89 he should regard as the true unknowns and which 68 he will have to fix by organised guesswork based on experience and analogy and nothing more. It is here that art truly merges with science, and for those with a spirit of adventure, where the excitement really begins.

In my undergraduate days I can remember a cutting from a newspaper being pinned on the engineering notice board with a typical student comment added. It described how a reservoir built in South Africa some ten years earlier had so far never been more than 10% full. The pencilled comment simply read 'Slide rule error?'

One of the most elaborate pieces of analogue engineering I have ever seen was carried out in Manchester in the 1930s by the late Professor A. H. Gibson whose last-ever course in hydraulics I was privileged to attend. He had been asked to predict the effect of the introduction of a tidal barrage in the Estuary of the River Severn. Now the number of equations needed to describe the three-dimensional shape of the river alone would have been formidable. But Professor Gibson was a master of the art of scale-modelling (one of the great arts of engineering) and he himself had sat at the feet of the great Osborne Reynolds, who had laid down the laws governing laminar and turbulent flow in fluids, and he knew that by scaling down lengths, he could also scale down time. So from historical records he built a scale model of the Severn Estuary as it had been in 1849, and set the model running (i.e. allowed the water to flow, erode and deposit) for several weeks until the model 'date' corresponded with the date of the experiment, i.e. 1927, when he was able to check from measurements of the actual sandbanks whether or not his model was a good one and, if not, to extract clues which would enable him to improve it. Engineering can often be a long and tedious process (but then so can building a particle accelerator for physics research) but finally Professor Gibson was satisfied with the accuracy of the model and was ready to insert the barrage and let the model run on.

This was an example of *extrapolation,* a process allied to, but infinitely more risky than, *interpolation,* both of which are illustrated in Figure 4.1 in a simple graph relating just two variables. From experiment, a number of points on the graph are known with a surety that experiment alone can provide. But information is sparse and the question is how the relationship works between points 4 and 5. The obvious guess is shown by dashes, but it could be any of the other

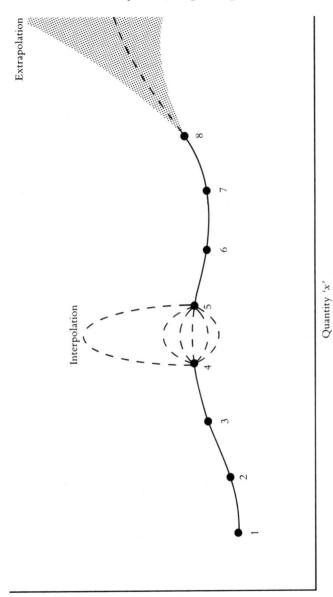

Figure 4.1   Interpolation and extrapolation are guessing games.

dashed curves, especially if any form of resonance phenomenon is suspected. This is interpolation. Extrapolation asks
the question: 'How does the graph continue beyond point 8?'
and even the dashed curve merges into a blur after a very
short excursion. Yet the engineer finds himself in this latter
situation more often than not, and by this I do not imply only
those probing the frontiers of knowledge. The run-of-the-
mill engineer is in just as hazardous a situation whether he is
predicting the performance of a new design of apparatus, or
the delivery date of the next batch of a well-tried product to a
customer in Newcastle.

TRIAL AND ERROR

Perhaps the most successful of all techniques, not only in
engineering, but in cooking, travelling, gardening—*living*(!)
is that given the name 'trial and error'. The strange thing is
that it is slightly frowned upon by the scientific Establishment, who must feel that somehow it is an inferior method to
that of mathematical prediction or even that of analogy—
almost an admission of failure of some kind. I suppose it is the
old spectre of 'craft' again, which like every other human
activity needs trial and error to achieve success. No child cuts
a perfect square from a piece of paper first time, let alone a
circle. No athlete achieves his best high jump first time, and
so on. What often surprises people is that despite their
wonderful eyesight they do not really know just where things
are. As the hand goes to pick up a pen, the eye, seeing the
hand to be off course, sends corrective signals to the brain,
and hand is guided to pen as a military missile is guided on to
its target by a process of feedback that is now a familiar part
of control theory. Control engineering has in fact become a
whole branch of its own in the engineering field, and of
course Nature, with something like 20,000 times the length of
experience of man in engineering matters (see Chapter 6) has
built it into all living systems. The human body is a mass of
control systems far more complex than anything that

engineering ever made. One has only to think of the process of driving a car with all the corrections that have to be made in the space of a second to realise that driving in today's traffic is impossible! So is playing the piano, if the pianist has to think what each finger is doing at all times.

If you claim that you really *do* know where things are, put both hands behind your back, right now, and then bring one out rapidly and put it on the full stop at the end of this sentence. Try it several times. Try it with your eyes shut. It is only easy if you can watch yourself doing it and use guiding signals from the eye at all times, just as the astronaut applies guiding impulses on the way to the moon. There is a similar test that I used to give to new members joining a table-tennis club of which I was match secretary for many years. Stand with feet together facing a wall at such a distance from it that you think you will just be able to touch it by raising one arm to the horizontal with forefinger pointed. When you think you have it right, raise the arm and try. I had a theory that if you bang your knuckles on the wall or leave more than a one inch gap, you will never make a first-class ball player at any game. But you are only allowed *one* try, because the process of learning is very rapid in simple tests such as this. But the process of feedback is so instinctive that when you are ready to test yourself, it is best to close your eyes before raising the arm or you will almost subconsciously lean the body to correct as you see how wrong you are going to be. One of the many things that a training in engineering gives you is a new awareness of the reality and relative positions of objects.

I suppose one could say that another basic difference in approach between that of a physicist and that of an engineer is that the former will use trial and error only as a last resort, whilst the engineer will, in many if not the majority of cases, use it first. In this respect we might claim to be born engineers, for the look of joy on a baby's face when it first discovers the phenomenon of gravitation is rarely to be matched (see also p. 21). After that, everything on the pram cover within reach goes over the side, orange by orange, for baby has discovered the consistency of Nature—it *always* works, and it will take perhaps another twenty years of solid training, specialising in physics latterly, for it to become convinced of Heisenberg's Uncertainty Principle, i.e. it isn't necessarily so! As the baby grows it will use trial and error more and more, whether it be in finding where the mouth is when trying to feed itself or discovering that sand pies and sand castles only stay together when the sand is damp. So we practise engineering all our lives and end up like the man in one of Molière's plays who suddenly discovered that all his life he had been speaking prose! You cannot say this about physics, nor about Latin. Little wonder then that engineering is a *natural* profession that can be practised, *was* practised before there was speech. The joy of engineering is the joy of discovery and of making things work in a new situation—just the ingredients that a baby has. Trial and error leads naturally to communication by imitation—'do it like this' need not be said by a child of one race showing a child of another with no common language, how to use a stick to hit stones into the sea.

But, like most things, trial and error has its limitations. An equally simple example to those given above, but at the other end of the scale, is the idea of building a power station to see if it gives the required output, in the hope of modifying it if the first shot proves unsatisfactory! (Money like this was spent on projects such as the Hawk Locomotive of the 1960s and more recently the APT.) Between these two extremes there is a whole range of situations where *judgement* is brought into play to decide whether or not a first shot, a scale model or similar manufactured thing is justified in order to save months of calculation and worry, and millions of pounds. When the first object is built and has to be seen by the paymasters to be 'nearly right', it gets called a 'prototype'. Prototypes can be designed to try out an idea, to be easily modified in as many ways as possible, to be put into service in an emergency, and so on. Although the word is usually applied to big things and big projects, there is no reason not to use it for new ideas to do with things as small and simple as matchboxes.

INDUCTION AND DEDUCTION

In a sense, trial and error resembles what is known as the inductive method of teaching in that you creep forward slowly into the unknown jungle, consolidating what has already been achieved, rather than being dropped in by parachute and thrashing about in all directions until you find the paths. In inductive teaching, of algebraic equations, for example, you begin with $2x = 6$, explaining that if 2 identical boxes, each containing the same unknown number of apples, together contain 6 apples, each box must contain 3 apples. Thus you discover the rule that allows you to divide each side by the same number. After doing dozens of similar equations and working up to such difficult ones as $1·69x = 41·7$ or $\sqrt{3x} = \sqrt{27}$ you move on to a more complex type of equation where $2x + 1 = 6$ and learn that you can add or subtract the same thing from each side. You are soon solving such equations as

$$\frac{5x - 3}{7x + 2} = 49.$$

That is inductive teaching—leading the student slowly by the hand into deeper and deeper jungle.

In deductive teaching you begin by simply stating the rules for solving the general equation:

$$\frac{ax + b}{cx + d} = e \qquad (4.2)$$

after which you may put $a = 2$, b and $c = 0$, $d = 1$ and $e = 6$ and obtain the solution to $2x = 6$ at once! What is more, equation (4.2) is ready to be programmed for computer and there is a tool that will solve *all* such equations but, alas, not all problems!

There was a time when the engineer believed in the inductive method absolutely, but those days are passing, and the great god Computer has had a fair hand in it I fear. I say 'fear', because deductive teaching is not the be-all and end-all of knowledge for it has two serious omissions. It neglects the *understanding* of the process, and worse, it can never go beyond the original so-called 'general case' and there is *always*, in the real world, a more 'general' problem than any that the human mind can imagine. So if inductive teaching is a passing phase, all I, as an old-fashioned engineer, can say is that I regret its passing.

When I was first introduced to Bessel functions by a mathematics teacher, he did it, knowing his audience to consist of 100% engineering undergraduates, by considering the practical problem of a heavy but flexible chain hanging from a hook and being given a horizontal, impulsive blow at the bottom end. The resulting equation none of us could solve. He explained that to do so, we would need to know how to multiply together two infinite series (also a new and 'impossible' idea to most of us). Finally he solved the equation and showed us that only a table of numbers, like log tables, would suffice to deal with the answer to the original practical problems. He went on to tell us that these were called Bessel functions and that they had a habit of turning up whenever there was cylindrical symmetry in the problem. Finally he showed us an easier way of finding Bessel functions from a very complicated formula, known as the 'generating function', but we could all see that at least it worked and, once having appreciated that it did, there was no need ever after to worry as to *why* it worked.

The following year we had repeat instruction in some parts of the maths course, including Bessel functions, with a different lecturer who appreciated not the mind of the engineer. I shall never forget his opening remarks on Day One.

'We shall first deal with Bessel functions. Consider the expression:

$$J_n(x) = \sum_{r = 0}^{\infty} \frac{(-1)^r}{\lfloor r \lfloor n + r} \left(\frac{x}{2}\right)^{n + 2r},$$

Well, I also remember my thoughts at the time: 'Anyone who has not met this before will be asking: why not consider some other equally stupid set of symbols and letters; why pick on that particular one?' And he never *did* explain why they were useful to engineers in solving real problems in a real world!

The fact that pure science is in its infancy is borne out by the desire among its teachers to tell the story of everything that has happened since the beginning. In the 1930s we were taught about William Gilbert picking up bits of paper with a charged rod to interest Queen Elizabeth I. Most textbooks on magnetism began with lodestones in the Chinese desert in 3000 BC. Then we were taken through Volta and Ampère, frogs' legs, Oersted, Faraday, Maxwell, and progressed to Pauli, Max Planck, Niels Bohr, Einstein and, if we were lucky, Heisenberg.

But we do not do this in engineering, as we do not do it in other subjects. We simply teach how to do it. Imagine a cookery course which began with Primitive Man accidentally throwing a bone on to a fire and being intrigued by the aroma!

Perhaps it would be a good idea if we *introduced* a little history into our engineering teaching, as propaganda if you like, for as described on pp. 11, 13, the men who shaped the blade of the plough did more for civilisation than did Michelangelo. The plough blade probably began with no more than a blunt stick dragged through the ground, but the developed article, perhaps thousands of years later, was of very sophisticated shape. One is bound to admit that it reminds us more of the leaf of a plant whose shape has probably evolved as a result of air flowing past the leaf. What better example of the use of analogy. Fluid flow, whether it be soil past a steel blade, or air past a fragile, paper-like substance, ultimately produces similar shapes.

In the same lecture in which John Lenihan described the introduction of the stirrup (see pp. 10, 11) he described other fascinating early pieces of engineering:

The agricultural revolution which occurred at about the same time was also linked with the technology of horse power. In earlier centuries, the ox was commonly used for ploughing and other agricultural tasks. Horses were not very serviceable, partly because their hooves were easily damaged and partly because their tractive effort was very limited. The ox yoke was inefficient when applied to a horse because, as soon as the animal took the strain, the neck strap pressed on the windpipe with discouraging results.

The nailed horse-shoe appeared during the ninth century and the modern type of harness, with a padded collar allowing the animal to exert full effort, was developed almost simultaneously. . . . The rise of the middle classes, the growth of commerce, industry and education and many other features of modern civilisation may be traced back to the agricultural revolutions—technological but not scientific—of nine or ten centuries ago.

Earlier in his lecture he had expressed the sentiment that I have often heard expressed among the Engineering Institutions.

It is often supposed that technology is the product of science, emerging unpredictably as a reward for untrammelled intellectual curiosity. The traditional view of this matter may be found in many official documents—most recently in the 1967 report of the Council for Scientific Policy. 'Basic research' the Council advised 'provides most of the original discoveries and hypotheses from which all other progress flows. . . . It provides the reservoirs of new concepts, examples of which subsequently prove to have more than theoretical significance and suddenly assume great economic and social utility'.

Clearly the view of the Establishment in 1967, and I suspect little changed in 1984.

REFERENCE

Nelkon, M. and Parker, P. (1977) *Advanced Level Physics* (4th edn). London, Heinemann Educational Books

5

Mathematics and Engineering

'God is a mathematician'. (*Sir James Jeans*)

Whilst on the one hand, it is a fact that every true engineer at one time or another in his/her career regrets the fact that their mathematical knowledge is inadequate for the problem, it is also remarkable how very much a good engineer can accomplish by means of mental arithmetic, plus an insight into the relationship between topology and mathematics. Thus if the problem deals with cylindrical structures and the engineer decides that a detailed quantitative study is called for, any formulation of the problem into equations that does not lead to Bessel functions must be wrong. On the other hand, a rough check on the voltage needed to produce a given amount of power in a particular electrical system may involve a simple calculation such as:

$$\frac{(29.6)^2 \times \pi^2 \times 2 \cdot 13 \times 10^{-8} \times 4500^2}{\sqrt{3} \times 0 \cdot 0071 \times 42 \cdot 6}$$

The modern student might be surprised to see the engineer handle it in the following way, never dreaming of bringing out his pocket calculator. The mental processes that take place include such things as:

'29·6 is virtually 30'
'π^2 is 10'
'4·5^2 is nearly 20'
'$\sqrt{3}$ is $1\frac{3}{4}$', and so on.

Applying this, term by term to the above expression, the engineer effectively replaces it by:

$$\frac{30^2 \times 10 \times 2 \times 10^{-8} \times 20 \times 10^6}{\frac{7}{4} \times 7 \times 10^{-3} \times 40}$$

Next he gets rid of the powers of 10, thus:

$$\frac{3^2 \times 2 \times 2 \times 10^2}{\frac{7}{4} \times 7 \times 4 \times 10^{-2}} = \tfrac{36}{49} \times 10^4 \approx 7500$$

The exact value to four significant figures, incidentally, is 7120, and this example was chosen at random and not so as to be especially amenable to this crude treatment.

So skilled does the engineer become at this that all that appears on the back of the 'old envelope' that was pulled out at the start of the calculation is:

$$\frac{(29 \cdot 6)^2 \times \pi^2 \times 2 \cdot 13 \times 10^{-8} \times 4500^2}{\sqrt{3} \times \cdot 007 \times 42 \cdot 6} = 7,500$$

This is, so to speak, one end of the scale. At the other end the design of so complex a piece of machinery as an induction motor requires an elaborate computer program to ensure that the designer is getting the best possible use out of the materials available.

Here now comes the problem of the 1980s which may well run into the next century. Every complex calculation involves a series of equations that are, so to speak, a translation of the physical factors involved, such as the size of the various pieces, the materials of which they are made, the properties of those materials and the physical laws, so far as they are known, that govern the behaviour of the various pieces in the light of the other information given.

NO MATTER HOW GOOD YOUR COMPUTER, IT WILL NEVER BE ABLE TO TRANSLATE THE REAL PROBLEM INTO A MATHEMATICAL PROGRAM.

Some human must do that; and when the program has been run the same human must be able to translate the numerical answers back into pieces of hardware. One engineer's interpretation of the problem of predicting the performance of a piece of equipment in terms of equations will be quite different from that of another engineer. *And neither can be said to be wrong.* They will give different emphasis to different aspects. They will ignore different side-effects. They have different amounts of experience, probably in different disciplines in their earlier life, and one will get a better answer than the other. This does not mean that, in the next problem, the same engineer will again get the better answer.

It is small wonder, therefore, that a lot of engineers tend to regard mathematics as a mere 'tool' among a whole bag of hypothetical tools needed to do the job in hand. Some even regard it as a necessary evil and welcome the computer and its programmer as one unit or 'thing' that will take the back-breaking part out of the job, much as a gentleman gardener employs a man to do the digging, weeding, forking and raking, whilst he merely plans the garden, sows the seeds and buys the plants.

In engineering there is never any 'black' nor any 'white'. *There are only shades of grey!* Every solution is at best a compromise in which one aspect is sacrificed in order to enhance another. In such a world the mathematical skill lies in estimating the degree of accuracy required in each stage of the problem and in some problems, accuracy at least as good as that required in pure science is necessary to achieve success. Pure scientists may have the concept of an electron microscope, or a radio telescope, but engineers *build* them. Which, would you guess, needed the greater accuracy in their mathematics?

Nevertheless, in the engineer's world there are no infinitely sharp corners, and on drawings of apparatus to be built, every corner is specified as having a radius, however small. A pencil line is recognised as having a thickness, which is why the machinist takes the measurements from the *figures* given on the drawing, rather than measuring the actual drawing, even though the latter has been drawn strictly to scale.

WHY DO WE NEED HIGHER MATHEMATICS IN ENGINEERING?

The image of the engineer that has persisted, despite the efforts of such mighty bodies as the Council of Engineering Institutions, is that of a man at a lathe, working to a drawing, from which he is required to turn a shaft to a certain size and accuracy, so that it shall fit another piece of metal that he will make tomorrow. Even the man who designs machines is only doing simple geometrical and trigonometrical calculations of the sixth-form kind, surely? And in electrical engineering it is all a question of putting circuits together, each of which will consist of resistors, capacitors and inductors, all of which we handled in school physics, is it not? As for the civil engineer who builds roads, dams and bridges, what is mathematical about shifting heaps of soil or constructing something from a very large-sized Meccano set?

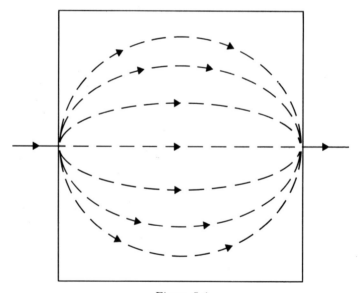

Figure 5.1

Perhaps the easiest way to answer these questions is by means of one or two examples. Being an electrical engineer I am naturally eager to describe electrical problems first. Figure 5.1 shows a thin sheet of copper which is part of a very simple electric circuit. The copper sheet is to be used as a heating element and in order to know how the heat generated as I^2R loss is distributed we need to know just where the current flows. The dotted lines give an idea of the form of the flow lines that we might expect. But how do you calculate them exactly? Then suppose that instead of a *thin* sheet, it was a *thick* sheet, in which an extra dimension must be taken into account. Now let us complicate the problem by feeding the circuit with *alternating current* so that inductive effects become even more important than resistive. I think you will agree that 'A' level physics is quite inadequate to solve such problems.

When it comes to the design of a radio transmitting system including the aerials, the problem again emerges rapidly as that of trying to see what goes on in a 3-dimensional space that appears to transmit electric and magnetic quantities, as it were, 'through nothing'. We are left with a set of rules, based on a mass of solid experimental evidence, and even though the quantities we deal with, such as electric and magnetic field intensities, can truly be said to be only figments of the mind, the aerial on the television set is real enough and there is a preferred shape to this piece of hardware that has to be worked out.

A mechanical engineer wrestles with problems of heat transfer and of fluid flow and there are similar kinds of problem to the electrical ones except that temperature difference replaces voltage, heat flow replaces electric current and there are thermal resistances and inertias (which may be thought of as thermal inductances) to take the place of their electrical counterparts. Again, the problems invariably involve 3-dimensional flow diagrams, whether of heat or of liquid or of gas.

When it comes to digging holes and piling up soil, there is a whole branch of science known as 'soil mechanics' and it might be worth your while to go into a local technical library, or failing that a technical bookshop, and just flick through the pages of a book on the subject and see just how much of it is pure mathematics. Soil, like fluids and the ether, occupies a 3-dimensional space, and the internal pressures vary from point to point in both magnitude and direction. What is more, they change with changing external conditions.

I hope that these very few examples will at least begin to focus your attention on the two fundamental reasons why higher mathematics is an *essential* tool of the engineer, no less than it is for his physicist colleague, alongside whom he or she often works.

(1) Nearly all the quantities, real or imagined, which are the medium in which the engineer must work to get real practical answers, occur in a 3-dimensional real world, so the quantities have a size and a direction which may be different at every point in space.

(2) Everything in the real world is subject to change. Even direct current heats up the circuit in which it flows, so the resistance of the circuit changes and Ohm's Law is no longer simple. There is a famous hymn that contains this line of wisdom:

> *'Change and decay in all around I see.'*

So all the quantities in (1) are constantly changing with time. The engineer is involved in *rates* of change with time, often with *rates of rates* of change. Where the quantities described in (1) change from point to point in space, there are spatial rates of change. They may also have rates of change with respect to time.

A thorough knowledge of calculus is as fundamental a tool to the engineer as is a paintbrush to the artist or a hammer to the stone-mason. Time rates of change are (d/dt)'s, space rates of change are (d/dx)'s except that because of the 3-dimensional nature of the quantities there are also (d/dy)'s and (d/dz)'s, and the rates of time change may be different in the 3 axes.

The complexity can become simply appalling!

Now for what might be described as the 'earthy' type of engineer, calculus is indeed perhaps something to be avoided or, at best, solved in the simplest possible manner. The 'earthy' one still regards dy/dx as the limit of $\delta y/\delta x$ where δy and δx are *very* small bits of x and y but finite and real nevertheless. The mathematician of equal educational standard has already taken on board the idea that dy/dx is just a symbol for a single quantity and not a fraction at all. So when the product $(dy/dx) \cdot (dx/dy)$ appears, the mathematician states quite firmly that it is equal to unity but abhors any suggestion that the answer was obtained (as the earthy engineer would obtain it) by cancelling the 'bits', thus (infinitesimal though they are):

$$\frac{\cancel{dy}}{\cancel{dx}} \cdot \frac{\cancel{dx}}{\cancel{dy}} = 1$$

Of course, the mathematician is right. You cannot write $(0/0) = 1$, but it takes a journey into the 3-dimensional world to jolt the engineer back to the truth of an amazing result that common sense could not possibly have predicted. In 3-dimensional space it is possible to cut a slice through any pair of axes and take the variations in the plane of the slice alone. This is called 'partial differentiation' and is written (if the slice is parallel to the x/y plane) as $\partial y/\partial x$.

Now the earthy, common–sense engineer is likely to treat the triple product $(\partial y/\partial x) \cdot (\partial x/\partial z) \cdot (\partial z/\partial y)$ by the same technique as before, cancelling the 'bits' in pairs top and bottom, to obtain again the answer 1.

But the correct answer is always -1! It is perhaps the first time in our careers, for most of us, that we get an indication that we do not understand 3-dimensional space.

But a simple experiment, repeated until the engineer is convinced that it must *always* be so, can transform the earthy, common–sense engineer into the more sophisticated kind who recognises that, like it or not, he or she is going to have to study vector calculus, and thereafter be elevated to the status of their physicist colleagues, so far as mathematical knowledge and needs are concerned.

The experiment is as follows:

Take a flat piece of board and a considerable quantity of Plasticine or other modelling clay, as shown in Figure 5.2. Now shape the clay in any way you wish. It can have holes through it like many of Henry Moore's famous creations, but

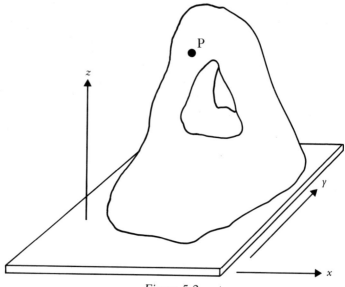

Figure 5.2

it must not include any infinitely sharp corners nor infinitely sharp edges. Now mark one particular point, P, anywhere on its surface. Decide on axes *x*, *y* and *z* and these can be quite arbitrary, but it is well to choose them conveniently, as in the example shown. Take a sharp knife and cut the model in the *x–z* plane for example, through the marked point, P. Separate the halves and draw the contour you see as a graph of *z* (vertical) against *x* (horizontal), marking the particular point, P. (The slope of the graph at all points is of course $\partial z/\partial x$.) Now push the halves of the model together again and cut it again through P, but this time in the *y–z* plane. Plot a second graph. Repeat the procedure for the *x–y* plane (horizontal in the example shown).

The three graphs should be plotted in strict rotation, i.e. if the first is *z* against *x*, the second must be *y* against *z* and the third *x* against *y*, so that each axis occupies one vertical and one horizontal position. The result, for the example shown, may look something like the graphs in Figure 5.3.

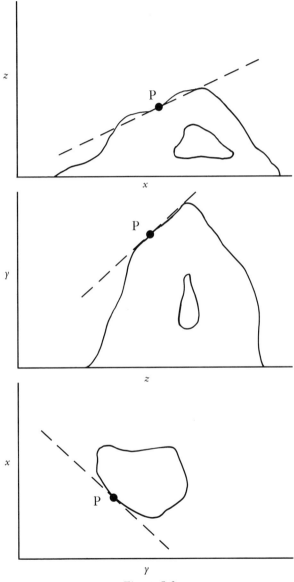

Figure 5.3

Note the slope of the curve as it passes through P in each case. There will always be 2 upward slopes and 1 downward or 2 downward and 1 upward—never all 3 in the same sense—and *there is no shape of solid object that you can make that will disobey this rule.*

This is the meaning of the minus sign in the triple product of the 3 partial derivatives.

It is a property of 3-dimensional space (or as we say these days for short: '3-space').

NATURAL SHAPES

In engineering, as in many facets of life, there is no substitute for experience. The great engineer Isambard Kingdom Brunel and his father Marc Brunel had such a physical insight into structures that they often predicted the collapse of a building within days, or in some cases hours, of the event taking place.

There is a parable told of three cannibals who were walking through a jungle when they came to a heap of skin and bones on the ground—the remains of a dead animal. They stopped and looked at the carcass for some time. Then one of them spoke: 'That must have been a very large animal', demonstrating at once that he was the physicist of his tribe, for he made a deduction from an observation. The second cannibal bent down and picked a small bone from the beast, sniffed it, licked it, threw it down. Clearly he was the chemist. Meanwhile the third man had been down 'on all fours' rummaging among the skin and bones, as if looking for something. He was in fact looking for the largest bone, for he had had an idea. When he found it, he was delighted to see that it had a large knob at one end and a small knob at the other. Holding it by the large knob he wielded it as a weapon and grunted. Then he turned it round and held it by the small knob. This time he grunted much louder and without more ado dispatched his companions with a heavy blow over the head. He was, after all, a cannibal.

But he was also an engineer and we see at once how much cruder he appears than his companions. We see also how he triumphs! But how do we know he was an engineer? There are two main reasons:

(1) He chose the largest bone and after one experiment held it by the smaller end. He did both of these things not because he knew about Newton's Laws of Motion, nor about the property of a body we call 'inertia'. *He did it because of his experience.*

(2) He also used analogy, as do all engineers, and because the bone reminded him of a club, laboriously carved out of wood, he used it as a club, to great effect.

What my experience has taught me is that the shapes of our manufactured articles are very different from the shapes of living things, whether it be plants, fishes, insects or animals. They are different also from the shapes of inanimate but natural things, such as river basins and deltas, which resemble trees and systems of arteries very closely, and crystal structures in magnetic material which resemble brain corals and the brains of animals.

We are still the children of Euclid in a world where straight lines and circles, cubes and regular polyhedra, right circular cones and spheres are almost sacrosanct. Think how many articles in the home are basically cylindrical. One of the reasons for this is that the process of turning is easier and cheaper than that of milling. What could be simpler than the potter's wheel? Yet Nature rejected the wheel, possibly for the best of reasons.

Falling back again on my experience I find that calculations involving our 'simple' shapes are often the most complicated. I have seen a thesis of some 300 pages whose sole purpose was the accurate calculation of the inductance of a large circular coil of relatively small cross-section.

Sir James Jeans, having seen the power of number theory in living things, principally those devised by the Leonardo of Piza, also known as Fibonacci, declared: 'God is a mathematician.' The record was put straight however by Stevens (1976) in his book *Patterns in Nature*. Stevens also discussed the Fibonacci numbers in relation to rates of growth and decay, but ended with the warning sentence: 'The plant is not in love

with the Fibonacci series; it does not seek beauty through the use of the golden section; it does not even count its stalks; it just puts out stalks where they will have the most room.'
I myself even began to wonder if we chose the best system of numbers, in that we defined unity as ourself. '*I* am one.' And having set foot on that road, we soon found ourselves incapable of calculating exactly such simple and fundamental quantities as the ratio of the circumference to the diameter of a circle, the natural growth and decay rate for all things that change their size or state and the Golden Ratio (φ) which turns up every time we try to make calculations on living tissue.

I mention these things here to show that an engineer is every bit as much a philosopher, every bit as much a fundamental thinker as his physicist or mathematical colleague. The one thing perhaps that divides them is that the engineer has to have that intuitive sense to know when the calculations have to stop and something has to be *made*—whether it be merely a decision, an experiment, or a sophisticated prototype of the final device.

THE AGE OF THE COMPUTER

The first Universal Digital Computer was launched on an unsuspecting world in Manchester in 1951. Within the year people, and especially mathematicians, were asking questions as to whether the computer could go ahead of its creators. Could it in fact 'think'? This opened up a whole new subject of cybernetics, and science fiction writers in particular had a field day.

When sanity returned most people were nevertheless left with the thought that the problems of the world, and the engineering world especially, had somehow become easier. 'All you have to do is stick it on the computer and let it do the worrying' was fundamentally the sentiment expressed. Courses on computer programming flourished. In 1952 a computer programmer was almost god-like and paid an appropriate salary. Within 20 years computer programmers had become of rather lower value (in real terms) than a dust-man or road sweeper—and were paid accordingly!

Whatever else it is, a computer is a slave designed to answer any question that can be put into numerical or even symbolic form—but nothing else. When the programmer asks it to look at the design of a complicated piece of machinery and to turn its 'random number generator' (seen by many as the equivalent of human free will) loose on various parameters, examining a wide range of alternative designs and applying criteria of quality to each new design, it certainly looks as if the 'box of electronics' really is capable of designing—even *inventing*—new and better machines, which its creator was incapable of doing.

But it was all built into the program.

Let me illustrate, by means of a few simple examples, the pitfalls of believing that if a problem is put on to a computer the answer is necessarily correct (assuming that the computer always works as designed):

(1) When a body moves in a circle at uniform speed it has an instantaneous acceleration towards the centre. Let us ask the computer to calculate this acceleration. If we calculate the radial distance r of the particle from the centre at all times and differentiate it with respect to time we shall get the radial velocity dr/dt. If we differentiate again we shall get the radial acceleration d^2r/dt^2 which is what we are required to find.

We program the computer to differentiate any expression for r in terms of time. Then print into the program this expression which happens to be $r = $ constant (k, say). The computer rapidly calculates $dr/dt = 0$, $d^2r/dt^2 = 0$, and prints out the answer that there is no such thing as centripetal acceleration!

What did we do wrong? We fed it an incomplete set of rules. We forgot to tell it that position, velocity and acceleration are *vector* quantities and that when a vector changes *direction* it can only do so by having an additional vector added to it. So a constant *numerical* value of r does not describe completely what is going on in circular motion. The computer has to be programmed to take account of the fact that a journey from A to B (Figure 5.4) followed by a journey from

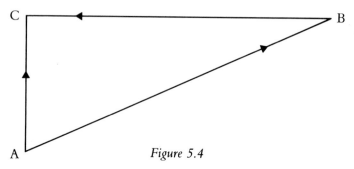

C   B

A   *Figure 5.4*

B to C, is equal to a journey from A to C. Thus in vector algebra 1 + 1 can equal ¼, however stupid this might seem to a lay person who knows nothing of vector algebra. The computer is in the same state until you educate it and record in the program that 'this next calculation is a vector calculation'.

Now comes the biggest danger of all. As soon as the rules of vectors have been established they are taken as the 'gospel' for all future calculations and as such they are then abused (by the programmer of course, *not* the computer).

Multiplication of vectors can be of two kinds:

(a) scalar multiplication, denoted **a . b** where the answer is (**ab** cos θ) in magnitude and has no direction, but θ is the angle between **a** and **b**;

(b) vector multiplication denoted **a** × **b** or $a \wedge b$ where the answer is (**ab** sin θ) in magnitude and has a direction which is perpendicular both to **a** and to **b**.

To readers who are not familiar with vector algebra, the above two rules must look like the traditional Double-Dutch, but let me again explain with the help of simple mechanical examples.

(2) Figure 5.5 shows a ring P being pulled along a rough wire AB by means of an elastic string PQ which is in tension. The problem is to find the work done against friction between ring and wire in travelling from, say, X to Y. Now work is a scalar quantity with no direction (you have to come to *know* this, mostly from experience and from thinking a lot

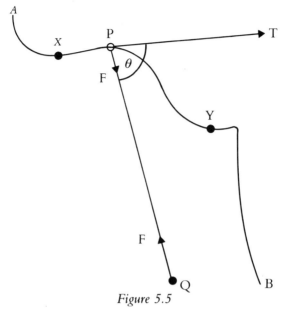

Figure 5.5

about it!). So the problem calls for a *scalar* product. At any point such as P, the ring is moving instantaneously in the direction PT. (The computer could be given enough data about the shape of the wire AB to be able to work out the direction PT at any point.) The elastic string is pulling with a force F along PQ, the size of the force depending on its length, which is for ever changing. (Again the computer could work this out.) The work is done only by the component of F that acts directly against the friction, i.e. by movement along PT (work done = force × distance). The computer is therefore asked to take a tiny bit of the wire of length δs and work out the product ($F \delta s \cos \theta$) for as many bits of the wire as you choose to divide it into (the more bits, the more accurate the answer, but the longer the computing time). The computer has in fact performed the vector algebra equation for the work W as

$$W = \int_x^y F \, . \, \mathrm{d}s$$

73

The example of a *vector* product is simpler, see Figure 5.6. If we wish to find the area of the parallelogram ABCD we can regard AB as a vector **a**, AD as a vector **b** and perform the vector product **a** × **b** to give a vector of size **a b** sin θ (well known to be the area of a parallelogram) and its direction is at right angles to the plane of the diagram. When you think of it, there can be no meaning to the *direction* of an area unless it is at right angles to its plane (something else you have to come to know by experience and by thinking a lot about it!).

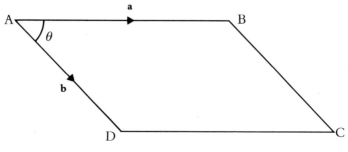

Figure 5.6

(3) Having established the rules for scalar and vector product for known cases where they clearly work, it is often glibly assumed that they work for anything! For example I have seen vector product used to 'explain' and to calculate centripetal acceleration (see Figure 5.7). The angular velocity of the particle P is ω given by $\omega = v/r$, and again the only sensible direction for ω is at right angles to its plane of spin (after thinking a lot about it, yet again!). So the vector product fanatic says, 'Fine, take the vector product of ω and v (which are at right angles for P) and you have a vector at right angles to both ω and to v and thus radially *inwards* (a rule established after a *lot* of experience and thinking about it) and of size $v\omega = v^2/r$. This of course is the correct answer, but the method is extremely dubious for the same velocity has been used twice!

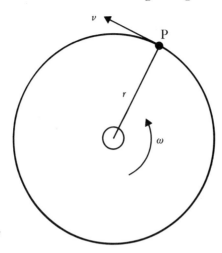

Figure 5.7

(4) However, now let us see the vector product addict come completely unstuck as he applies the same rule to the calculation of the tangential acceleration experience by a ring P which is sliding outwards at a velocity v along a radial wire which is rotating at angular velocity ω (see Figure 5.8). This acceleration gives rise to the force known as the 'Coriolis' force, at which name the strongest of mechanical engineers have been known to tremble! Proceeding with the vector product technique, with surely a lot more justification than in the centripetal case, for the two velocities are now quite separate, we arrive at: acceleration $= v \times \omega$ which is $v\omega$ at right angles to both v and ω, i.e. tangential as shown. Alas! The Coriolis acceleration is $2\,v\omega$ in that direction so half of the true answer got lost in the process. The vector product only calculated the half due to v changing direction (as in the centripetal case) and forgot that the tangential velocity $r\omega$ was increasing also because r was increasing.

I hope that these examples will serve to show how dangerous it can be to believe in rule-of-thumb answers obtained by computer. Tomorrow's top engineers will be those who know enough physics and mathematics to be sure that they have asked the computer to solve the *right* equations, not equations relating to some other problem.

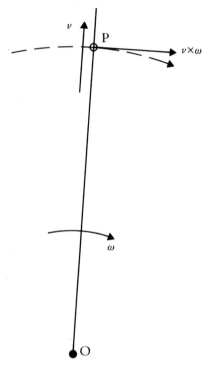

Figure 5.8

There is no easy way out via the computer. Engineers will always need to know the physical world, their physics and their mathematics!

TRIAL AND ERROR AGAIN

One of the greatest advantages of a computer, however, is that it can relieve the engineer of the often incredibly laborious process of trial and error discussed in Chapter 4. The technique is most useful to engineers when there are far too many unknown quantities and far too few equations even to make a crude guess at a formal solution. The engineer writes down design quantities (from experience) which are at least sensible and would produce a machine that would work, however badly, inefficiently, costly, etc. Then he changes one dimension at a time, gradually, at each step noting whether the result is a better or a worse machine. When an optimum is reached he leaves the dimension fixed and changes another. When the second has been optimised he must return to the first and re-work it, for it does not follow that what was best for dimension A with dimension B at value B_1 is still best when B changes to B_2. This technique is known as 'hill-climbing' for it resembles looking for a peak in 2 dimensions at once, as one does when climbing a mountain. Of course, the engineer usually has many more than 2 dimensions to optimise and the amount of labour required to keep returning to earlier parameters can become enormous, which of course is just where a computer becomes vital, because of its speed.

This whole process has long been known in the mathematical world as 'iteration' to give it a more respectable name than anything that even suggests that guessing is involved. The engineer has no qualms at all about declaring it to be 'organised guesswork'. Long before the days of pocket calculators, the engineer had abandoned log tables for their mechanical analogue, the slide rule (accurate only to 3 figures), which was long known affectionately in the profession as a 'guessing stick'!

There are occasions, of course, where unless the designer is prepared to fix a large number of parameters of the system at the outset, there is no framework on which to perform any kind of iteration at all, and it is at this point that the process of engineering resembles an art more than it does a science. The engineer may even resort to philosophies as shaky as simply saying: 'What looks good will *be* good!'—but there is a wealth of past experience to back it up. The streamlined shape of a car suggests speed, even to a small child. It could therefore be said to be, at least in part, instinctive. This of course is used by the sales engineer, for streamlining of a car for use below 70 mph has little effect on performance, but a huge effect on sales!

The elegant shape of a cooling tower for a power station, the intriguing lattice of struts and ties in the Forth Bridge and the orderliness of the keys on a piano keyboard are all examples of things that are both beautiful and functional. They look good and *are* good.

Before the digital computer assumed its supreme eminence, analogue computers of considerable complexity were to be found here and there—simple ones too, of which the slide rule is a classic example, often quoted by pre-digital authors wishing to point out the distinction between analogue and digital. The cash register was usually quoted as the equivalent classical example of a digital computer. It used to be pointed out that whilst designers of machinery were satisfied to calculate the diameter of cooling pipes to 3 significant figures, a customer in a shop would be unhappy to receive change for a £10 note to the nearest 6d! The accuracy of the analogue computer was said to depend only on the accuracy to which the apparatus could be built whilst the cash register was *correct*.

But of course this over-simplified the problem and the philosophy behind analogue and digital methods. The accuracy of the digital computer depends on the number of significant figures which the programmer has allowed before 'rounding off'. The analogue computer is used where the digital can never be of use because the equations of the system are too complicated to be formulated. A good example of this is the model of the Severn Estuary constructed by the late Professor Gibson and described in Chapter 4. 'Oh,' exclaims the layman, 'that isn't a computer, that's just a model!'— Quite so, that is what is really meant by analogue computation. A slide rule is a model in wood of the equation:

$$\log x + \log y = \log xy$$

and lengths proportional to $\log x$ and to $\log y$ are effectively placed end to end and their total length 'anti-logged' to give the product of x and y.

Both digital and analogue methods therefore have their

limitations. The digital I have already discussed in relation to being sure that the equations fed to the computer are relevant and correct for the problem. In the case of analogue prediction the problem is almost the same, i.e. have you got the correct model? One can even go to the pure scientist and ask him if his model of an atom is correct. In the 1930s he would certainly have said 'yes' with confidence. But the thinking that has taken place in the last half-century has so changed that simple model that the present-day answer is bound to be 'We don't know.'

With engineers their model-making problem is often one of scaling. Before building a large machine would it not be very easy and most reassuring of success to build a ½0 scale model and test its performance? Alas the laws of Nature do not allow it. Such a simple quantity as the electrical resistance of a piece of wire will serve as example. If a wire of length l and diameter d has resistance R, then a similar wire of length $2l$ and diameter $2d$ has a resistance $R/2$. The surface area of the thicker wire is four times that of the thinner, so for the same cooling conditions the thicker wire can dissipate four times the heat loss within the wire. Heat loss is proportional to (current)^2 × resistance. Thus the current-carrying capacity I_2 of the thicker wire is related to that of the thinner wire I_1 such that

$$I_1^2 R = \tfrac{1}{4} I_2^2 \frac{R}{2}$$

or

$$I_1 = \frac{1}{2\sqrt{2}} I_2$$

But the ratio of the current density ($J = I/A$ amps per unit area of cross-section) in the two wires is such that

$$J_1 A = \frac{1}{2\sqrt{2}} J_2 (4A)$$

or

$$J_1 = \sqrt{2} J_2$$

Thus whilst the smaller wire can only handle roughly one

third of the current of the larger, it does so at nearly one and a half times the current density.

What is immediately interesting is that the Institution of Electrical Engineers' regulation for current density in household wiring used to be fixed at 1000 amps per square inch. So the law makers must have assumed that all household wiring can be regarded as being the same thickness!

But it is when you have to mix the disciplines and scale water flow and electricity, for example, that 'nothing fits'; and the worst enemy of all in scaling is *friction*. School physics teaches that there is a coefficient of friction which is constant. How convenient!—how thoughtful of the Creator to make it so! Do you really think it is as easy as that?

In the Christmas Lectures at the Royal Institution in 1966 I did an experiment in scaling friction which is worth describing here. Polished brass blocks measuring $2'' \times 2'' \times \frac{1}{2}''$, $1'' \times 1'' \times \frac{1}{4}''$, $\frac{1}{2}'' \times \frac{1}{2}'' \times \frac{1}{8}''$, $\frac{1}{4}'' \times \frac{1}{4}'' \times \frac{1}{16}''$ and $\frac{1}{8}'' \times \frac{1}{8}'' \times \frac{1}{32}''$ with optically flat faces were placed on a flat, clinically clean, hard surface which was then tilted slowly until the blocks began to slide down the incline. If the coefficient of friction is really constant, all the blocks should start moving together. But of course the biggest block moved first, when the plane was at only a very small angle to the horizontal. The others followed in order of size, the smallest adhering to the surface so that it was retained with the plane vertical! This last effect was due to electrostatic charge that had been built up as the result of polishing the flat surface.

What *really* happens in a situation like this is that no large surface is ever perfectly flat, not in terms of molecular distances. Therefore in general, two 'flat' surfaces can make contact initially in only 3 points. If these points consist of only 2 or 3 molecules, the *pressure* of the block, even a very small block such as the smallest of the 5 described here, is of the order of tonnes/cm^2 and the material at the 3 points literally *melts* over a small area, allowing more molecules to come into contact, making the contact areas greater and probably introducing a 4th, smaller area of contact and possibly a 5th. When the pressure is thus reduced (by increased contact area) below that required to melt the surface the system stabilises.

The frictional force per contact area is much more likely to be nearly constant than is any physical law about ratio of frictional force to normal force. When the plane is tilted, the force of gravity down the plane, on each block, is $M_g \sin \alpha$ where α is the angle of the plane. Opposed by a *constant* frictional force, the block with the largest mass M will naturally move first. It is an experimental and largely empirical fact that with less flat surfaces that are dirty, $F = \mu R$ is more likely to give good answers than $F =$ constant!

Where now your mathematics? The simple message is clear. When dealing with friction—beware!

No section on scaling (which was the subject that led me to friction) would be complete without a mention of its history. The first man to recognise that scaling was not as simple as multiplying everything by the same number and keeping all quantities in the same ratio was Leonardo da Vinci, perhaps the only man to contain the whole of knowledge in one brain, at his time. Obviously no one will ever do it again, because of the explosion of knowledge, but Leonardo, in considering some of his war machines, asked himself the question in his writings: 'If it takes an ounce of gunpowder to fire a pound of shot, how much gunpowder will it take to fire two pounds of shot?' I need hardly add that he knew the answer was not 'Two'.

REFERENCE

Stevens, Peter S. (1976) *Patterns in Nature*. Harmondsworth, Penguin Books

6

Living Machines

'We are the keepers of secrets for we walked the earth when it was young.'

(Fictitious remark attributed to an African elephant)

Among the many fallacies that have persisted in schools in the UK for most of this century is the one that biology is only useful to those who are going on to be doctors or dentists or veterinary surgeons. Sometimes it is grouped with geography or even arts subjects, perhaps because some see it as little more than classification on the grand scale. Perhaps it is the enormity, the diversity or the complexity of the subject, or all three, that keeps it out of the 'elite' subjects of physics and mathematics where everything is ever so *tidy*. If the human machine is more complex than anything that humans themselves have made, how shall we handle a million species of insect?

The geneticist J. B. S. Haldane was asked in his riper years by an interviewer what his experiences in life had led him to believe about the nature of the Almighty. Without hesitation he replied: 'He had an insatiable affinity for beetles!'—over 450,000 species.

The facts about biology are that whilst mankind has practised pure science (with any sort of intensity) for about 200 years, engineering can be traced back among humans for 30,000 years, but Nature has been practising it for 800,000,000 years. True, it had only one method, if we are to believe classical evolutionary theory, and that is trial and

82

error, rejecting the inferior at all times and hoping that the better things will emerge by accident. Nevertheless, over that sort of time scale, Nature has tried many more mechanisms and many more processes than we have even yet imagined, and the evidence for that statement is only just beginning to pour in.

Bio-engineer John Lenihan (1972) points out how ready we are to ascribe new functions to living organs, once we have discovered something new for ourselves. Of the human ear, he has this to say:

To Helmholtz the ear was a harp—a system of resonators allowing the analysis of complex sounds. Later it became a telephone (with the auditory nerve as a cable and the frequency analyser hidden in the brain) and more recently was found to embody such technical novelties as impedance matching, frequency analysis and automatic gain control. The brain, once thought of as a telephone exchange and then as an electronic computer, now turns out to be a holographic data storage system. . . .
  Physiology, like history, must be re-written in every generation if it is to be more than a collection of anecdotes.

All that appears to happen when a well-known engineering principle is seen to be working in living things is that we credit Nature with being 'clever' for having discovered it. What should happen is that we should recognise how 'thick' we are for not having noticed it sooner and saved ourselves the trouble of inventing it 'the hard way'.

A simple example will perhaps bring home the point. The Victorian horse-drawn carriages were very top-heavy, especially when loaded with people. The roads were very bad, often unpaved and rutted, and carriages frequently toppled. An engineer, applying scientific principles to the problem, found that the solution lay in designing the coach in such a way that, even when loaded, the centre of gravity of the whole was *lower* than the points from which it was suspended. Henceforth carriages were designed like the modern baby's pram, the coach proper hanging from high support springs, a mechanism that was given the name 'underslung chassis' and its inventor hailed as a genius.

I have no idea how many years elapsed between the principle being adopted for all manner of vehicles and a biologist observing that most spiders and beetles and even some insects with wings use exactly the same principle. We should have been good enough, surely, to have asked why the legs of all of these creatures went first *upwards* from the body and then down, making the appearance somewhat grotesque, even loathsome in the case of spiders. But a spider is very vulnerable when turned on to its back. Some beetles cannot open their wing cases so that if they ever get on their backs on a smooth surface they die a slow death of starvation. It is therefore vital to these creatures to have a very stable platform on which to stand and the broad-based, underslung body was the answer—*and we should have noticed!*

But there are other examples where it would have been virtually impossible for us to have seen what was going on and learned from it. A classic case is that of the electric eel. For centuries it was known that this creature could make a human unconscious or kill a lesser creature by electric shock. It was always assumed that this was the one and only purpose of the eel's battery. It was for self-defence, or to kill prey. During World War II we developed radar through our own ingenuity and sheer brain power. But in the 1950s someone had enough curiosity to put a probe into a tank of water containing an electric eel, to amplify the output and feed it to an oscilloscope. What they saw was a beautiful array of equally-spaced, constant amplitude pulses, emitted by the eel. It had been using OUR radar for millions of years!

It had also learned how to short-circuit the battery through an enemy and turned the battery into a *dual purpose instrument*. Nature is riddled with devices with two or more properties. Our own mouth, for example, is a hole for the intake of solid and liquid 'fuels'. It is an amplifying cavity for the vocal cords when we wish to communicate by sound. It can be used as a weapon in a fight, as a crude sort of wood tool or as a tactile 'magnifying glass' to prevent us from swallowing hard objects.

Up to a point we drifted into the dual-purpose instrument in engineering. It was almost inevitable. A delegate at a recent engineering conference, whose theme was 'Designing for fitness of purpose', pointed out that the shafts of all screwdrivers are much too thick ever to be in danger of being twisted off in shear due to trying to take out a rusty screw. So the excess metal is wasted?—Not really, he pointed out, 'or how do the rest of you get your paint can lids off?' The common screwdriver is probably used more as a lever than as a twister. I have seen it used for removing bottle tops, for stirring tea, and it is often used as a chisel. Nature would approve, but not the accountant! The latter wants to sell *one* instrument for *one* purpose. In that way you sell more instruments and make more profit. It is, in fact, quite difficult to make a tool that has only one purpose. Even a bank cash card is said to be capable of forcing door locks! But I have long believed that the accountant reached his zenith in the British Rail tea stirrer—a plastic strip weakened by a slot in it so that it can never be a screwdriver or chisel, is too thick to be a tooth pick, not sharp enough to be a scriber, cannot pick locks, peel apples or open packets of sliced bacon. It can only stir drinks! There you have the two extremes and it is obvious that it only makes sense, in the long term, to copy Nature.

HIGH TECHNOLOGY

But surely Nature's engineering is restricted to very basic things like levers and sail planes and thermal insulation? Our technology has now reached the levels of holography, fibre optics, liquid crystals and similar 'near miracles'. Living creatures have surely never attained such skills?

Be alerted by the electric eel example. Then go looking for the modern miracles of technology and you will not have to do more than superficial reading of elementary biology books to find what you seek. Again a single example will suffice to illustrate what we *ought* to be doing. The wings of certain species of butterfly and moth have a metallic sheen which is unlike the colours of 'ordinary' butterflies. The blue 'Morpho' species of Brazil are so well endowed in this splendour that they often find themselves built into jewellery as the centre piece. Similar colours occur in the wing cases of beetles, the feathers of humming birds and the scales of fishes, especially the small tropical species such as the 'neon tetra', so popular in household aquaria.

This colouration is different from that of ordinary pigment. The latter fades in daylight after the creature dies. But the metallic, almost iridescent colours will remain undiminished for 10,000 years and more, because the colour comes from the mechanical structure of the surface rather than from a pigment, which is almost pure chemistry. It has just been discovered that the mechanism of the 'metallics' is that of a liquid crystal.

Now the plot thickens. So far we have used liquid crystals for such things as displaying numbers on pocket calculators; in fact, for only such purposes as make use of the properties of liquid crystals that they change colour on application of a voltage across them, or of a radical change in temperature. But the butterflies and beetles and fishes and birds do not change colour. Certainly they have no voltages applied to them! The colours they display can rarely be classified as camouflage—almost the reverse. Nor are they particularly 'warning colours', e.g. the ocherous colour that is Nature's label for 'poison'. We must come to the alarming conclusion that we do not yet know all the properties of liquid crystals, nor yet make use of the principal one!

HERE ARE THE ANSWERS. WHAT ARE THE QUESTIONS?

There are so many places to go looking in biology that the problem is really where to begin. It would be unfair to say that we have not made a start. There are living organisms that can perform technological processes that we cannot yet organise, so we get the creatures to do it for us. For example, in extracting metals from ores the process is often very expensive in terms of energy. But it has recently been found that certain species of bacteria can reduce the costs considerably and reduce the pollution associated with the process. For example the bacterium *Thiobacillus ferrooxidans* converts iron in the bivalent form (Fe^{++}) into the ferric or trivalent form (Fe^{+++}). The bacteria involved are among the most remarkable life forms known. They are said to be chemo-lithotrophic ('rock-eating'). They obtain energy from the oxidation of inorganic substances. Many are autotrophic in that they capture carbon directly from carbon dioxide in the atmosphere. They live in environments that would be quite inhospitable to other organisms where for example the concentration of sulphuric acid is very high. Some heat-loving species require temperatures above 50°C and a few strains can live near the boiling point of water.

Two American engineers, R. Igor Gamow and John F. Harris, writing in the journal of the American Institute of Electrical and Electronics Engineers, *Spectrum,* in August 1972 said:

If one could discover the nature of the glue with which barnacles bind themselves so avidly to surfaces, even inert ones such as Teflon, and bottle this substance, one might reap a fortune.

They went on to list a number of instances where Nature's engineering feats exceed those of our own. There is a sporangiophore, for example, that can detect a single photon of light and is used to detect flaws in supposed light-tight rooms, etc. After a few hours the head of the fungus will have grown so as to point to the direction from which the single stray photon came. Many species of snake have an infra-red detector capable of distinguishing a temperature difference of 0·001°C from ambient. Thereby they detect the presence of such creatures as *Homo sapiens* from body radiation!

The situation may be summed up very well by saying that Nature's problems have all been solved. We only have to be clever enough to unravel the answers.

It has long seemed to me that far from being almost the outcast of scientific subjects at 'A' level, not to be compared in value to physics, maths and chemistry, biology ought to become the *basic* science that *all* should study with maths or chemistry as the reject—if indeed reject there has to be.

Nobel prizewinner Max Delbrück often remarked that when a physicist or engineer starts work on a biological problem, he is usually concerned that he does not know enough biology. It invariably turns out that he does not know enough physics or engineering. The use of liquid crystals just described is a classic example of this.

Difficult as it may seem, at first sight, there are some answers to which the questions can be worked out, and very useful lessons they make. The question of size, for example, leads directly to the topic of scaling or scale-modelling, which is of great importance in many engineering problems.

There are two main classes of living creature that have mastered the art of flight. One is the bird and the other the insect. The simplest of observations shows that the birds are a whole order bigger than the insects in general, the smallest humming bird just being comparable with the largest insect. Yet there is also clearly a limit to the largest bird that can fly, and there are flightless birds such as the ostrich that are bigger than this. An examination of the bird situation shows that whilst the available lifting forces come principally from the wings and are proportional to wing area, i.e. to $(length)^2$, the weight to be lifted is proportional to the volume and therefore to $(length)^3$, so to double every linear dimension is to multiply the lift by 4 and the weight by 8, and you clearly cannot go on scaling up for ever.

The limits that fix the size of the smallest bird must clearly be different. Here it is a question of maintaining the food supply through the hours of darkness and although Nature has proved herself extremely ingenious and most adaptable, some tiny birds even descending to a state near to that of short-term hibernation every night, a limit is finally reached in the case of the Bee Humming Bird, which weighs only 1·6 grams.

But what of the insects? How can it be that they take over at the small end of the bird range with such ease? In the first instance insects wear their skeletons on the *outside* of their bodies, whilst birds (like mammals) wear them on the inside. There is therefore a lot less flesh on the insects, many of which are little more than hollow shells, skeletons included, so the feeding problem is not acute. So why do they stop at the Goliath beetle as the heaviest insect (weight 70–100 grams)? Again the limits are imposed by a quite different set of constraints. Insects have no lungs and have adopted a system for extracting oxygen from the air by means of a series of tubes called 'spiracles'. But they rely on the air finding its own way down the tubes by diffusion. There is no pumping action, as in the case of lungs, and there is a very precise limit to the maximum depth to which the air will diffuse at a sufficient rate to support the life of the creature.

What is less well known is that not all insects are capable of flight, where flight is defined as self-propulsion through still air (as opposed to drifting along in the breeze, which many of course do). As in the case of birds, the engineering reasons are more obscure than they are at the other end of the scale. As the size of a solid object is reduced, the viscous drag of air increases in a manner that suggests that the air is becoming more like a liquid than a gas. So very small insects with wingspans of ony 3 or 4 mm have adapted their wings to become like the oars of a rowing boat. They consist of a stiff bristle along the leading edge which carries a series of fine hairs streaming out behind giving the appearance, to the naked eye, of a solid wing. But the action of the hairs is to billow out on a backward stroke and present a high frictional resistance to motion through the air, forcing the insect forwards. On the forward stroke the hairs lie parallel to each other in a plane and offer little resistance. It is one of the many natural examples of a ratchet. But when the insect is smaller still, the air has become as treacle and even rowing through it is impossible.

Similar rules govern the mammal kingdom. The maximum size of mammal is limited to that which can support itself on its legs without crushing its own bones with its own weight. The extinct Great Hairy Mammoth holds the record, but of course several Dinosaurs, and several species of whale (happily still with us) exceed this, for the former took most of their weight on their bellies, where it was largely distributed, whilst the whale's weight is fully distributed along its entire length.

THE LAWS OF PLANET EARTH

Now it would be easy to describe each of these size limits as due to some physical property of air, or water or bone, but the real basic reason behind them all is that we live on a planet of a certain size and density. This fixes not only the gravitational pull on mammals directly, but also the density of the atmosphere at ground level, its viscosity and the atmospheric pressure, and these all affect breathing, wing lift, wing drag and so on; on a different planet, creatures would occupy a very different size range. We will return to the question of size range in a moment, after first examining whether there are comparable laws of Planet Earth in purely engineering terms where pure metals and inorganic chemistry only are involved.

Sure enough there is a parallel set of rules with remarkable resemblance to those of living creatures. The common d.c. generator which feeds its own field coils, for example, is a direct inverse of bird flight. The power required to feed the field rises in proportion to $(length)^2$, the power output to $(length)^3$. This time it is the *desirable* quantity which carries the greater power and so there is a smallest size of shunt generator which is capable of supplying its own field. This smallest size can be pushed as low as possible by increasing the speed, until centrifugal force bursts the armature.

There is a longest length of chain or rope or string that can be suspended from a single top support, for no matter how strong the material, the addition of more and more weight to the bottom end ultimately breaks it immediately below the point of support.

The late Sir Frederic Williams, pioneer of the modern computer, once calculated that if humans had been only 1 inch high when fully grown, electrical engineering as a subject would have been virtually unknown for all electricity would have to have been supplied chemically at a cost of some 20–30 times that which is supplied from the huge turbo alternators of our present power stations. The development of the subject, due to the ready availability of the supply, undoubtedly aided its progress towards even the 'light current' subjects of valves, transistors, power electronics and communications which might not otherwise have blossomed until well into the 21st century, even though they were relevant to small creatures as well as to large.

This lesson can be extended to ask the question: What are we 'missing' because we are the size we are? One obvious answer is individual flight by our own muscle power. Even such 'giants' as Leonardo da Vinci were tempted to try, and they were still trying in this century, imagining that half a century of human experience could match millions of years of evolution, just because of the development of slightly better materials for the wings. They all failed because they were unaware that we are in the ostrich-size bracket, destined to be grounded so long as we are on Planet Earth. Whether we could have developed personal flying kit for moon visitors is an academic question, since the moon has no atmosphere in which to fly, and *that* of course, for precisely the same reason that keeps us on the ground here on earth, i.e. the size and density of the moon, but now too little instead of too much. It appears that so long as light gases constitute the atmosphere, flight size will always be fixed for all planets.

But there are more obscure pieces of engineering where size is less obvious as an all-powerful factor governing success or failure. In the 1950s a new British invention, code-named Zeta, was hailed as the first direct conversion of atomic energy into electricity. The trouble with atomic power stations as we knew them then, and *still* know them, is that they are no different from oil-fired or coal-fired stations in their worst aspect. The conversion of the primary energy has to go through the process of making *steam* on the way. And making steam to make mechanical power to drive electrical machines is expensive and inefficient. The electric generator is in the 96–98% efficiency bracket but the steam turbine is down in the 30–40% region.

Now Zeta promised to use the 'pinch effect' in a plasma to convert the atomic fission process into electric current *directly* in the one apparatus. The potential was enormous and fairly large sums of money were spent in development which came to nothing. What worries me is that at the end of the day I am not sure that the directors and planners were *ever* aware that they were fighting precisely the same kind of battle as that to produce individual man-powered flight—the law of size as affected by the laws of Planet Earth—and that had humans been 30 feet tall and been able to survive, Zeta was most definitely 'on'.

A similar but more marginal subject is that of the magneto-hydrodynamic (MHD) generation of electricity from a high-speed plasma moving past magnetic poles. The fact that success was temptingly nearer than it was in the case of Zeta simply caused more money to be poured into the effort of doing it, but I believe it still remains one of the ostrich family —a smaller species of ostrich perhaps, but still one destined to stand on the ground and flap its wings in frustration.

One further example is to be able to build much taller buildings. Termites have been known to build a column whose height is 2500 times the length of a termite. If we could build a tower in the same proportion it would be nearly three miles high (half the height of Mount Everest). For soil mechanics, as for almost all engineering subjects, scaling is never linear.

Earlier in this chapter I mentioned size range, and it is interesting to compare the ranges covered by various types of creature with at least one range of manufactured articles. The list below shows the weight ranges for various living creatures and for electric motors and generators.

Seeds	$2 \cdot 2 \times 10^{10}$
Mammals	$1 \cdot 9 \times 10^{8}$
Mammals (excluding whales)	$2 \cdot 0 \times 10^{7}$
Birds	$7 \cdot 8 \times 10^{4}$
Birds (including prehistoric)	$2 \cdot 3 \times 10^{5}$
Snakes	$7 \cdot 8 \times 10^{5}$
Insects	$2 \cdot 0 \times 10^{7}$
Flowers	$5 \cdot 8 \times 10^{9}$
and then	
Electric motors and generators	$6 \cdot 2 \times 10^{8}$

Apart from the birds and snakes, the remainder are remarkably high, yet only the plants and their seeds exceed the range of the man-made articles.

We must be ever-conscious of the laws of Planet Earth. They are more constant and more powerful than any law of physics. Yet of course they embrace many laws of physics in what we might call their 'internal structure'; and we shall learn about them most easily through the teaching of biology.

Sometimes one may be fortunate enough to see a fleeting reference to the subject in a physics textbook, as I was when I was at school and the following sentiment expressed in a book entitled *Properties of Matter* intrigued me all through my subsequent education. It ran something like this: 'If a man and an earwig walk over a cliff, the man falls to his death but the earwig floats down unharmed. But if both are soaked with water, the man suffers little ill-effect but the earwig will most certainly drown.' There was no comment or explanation to follow, so far as I remember, which might have been no bad thing, for it placed the reader in a typical engineering situation—a 'Here are the answers, what are the questions?' predicament. The subjects involved, of course, are 'terminal velocity' in free fall in air, in the first case, and surface tension in the second.

Terminal velocity is a question of scaling, very closely allied to that of flight. It has been said that if a spider is dropped down a mineshaft it simply wonders why it has gone dark! A mouse waits patiently to arrive at the floor, then runs away. A cat survives the fall. An alsatian dog is killed, a horse is smashed and an elephant explodes. Men and women have exploited their terminal velocity to perform in aerobatic teams in free fall 'circuses' but they all have to resort to parachutes for landing, although there have been cases of humans landing in a 'friendly' place (like a tree-covered bog) and surviving a fall from an aircraft.

Surface tension drowns the earwig because the force does not scale down with size (so water rises to a remarkable height in a very thin-bore tube dipped into it) and the water envelops the earwig in a skin-like water structure which its muscles are too weak to penetrate.

MOVING ABOUT THE EARTH

When it comes to transport vehicles there is an amazing set of comparisons with creatures that move about on land, in water or in the air. First of all, both our engineered machines and Nature's 'vehicles' have bilateral symmetry. The need to have a front and a back creates the concept of 'left' and 'right', and manœuvrability demands the symmetry.

Professor Gilbert Walton (1964) has written brilliantly on the comparison between the living machine and the man-made vehicle when it comes to creatures that move about the earth.

Outwardly in an animal, as in a motor car or ship, there is bilateral symmetry. Inside, however, the organs or components are not all arranged symmetrically; the heart is on one side in a mammal, and the carburettor is on one side in a car. It is easy to understand why the steering wheel in a car (not for export) is always on the right, but it is less obvious why hearts are not disposed equally to left or to right. In the final detail the loss of symmetry is complete. The molecules of haemoglobin in the blood, or of enzymes in the muscles, are apparently specially fabricated in a highly irregular but precise manner just as the details, for example, of the electrical system of a vehicle are completely irregular and show no symmetry. The comparison can be pursued further. Our right hand is a mirror image of our left hand, but a glucose molecule for instance in the tissue of our right hand is not a mirror image of a glucose molecule in the tissue of our left hand. Both are 'dextro rotary' and 'laevo' glucose plays no part. This complexity is the same in artificial things. The right side mudguard of a car is the mirror image of the left side mudguard, but nuts and bolts in both mudguards have right handed threads.

It would be nice to think that we had accepted Nature's land creatures as superior engineering and copied them in every facet as a quick way to development. The pipe system as a simplified bowel arrangement, leading to the exhaust pipe as the anus. The electric wiring as a very crude copy, but nevertheless a copy, of the nervous system, and the nuts and bolts that put it all together as the all-important glucose molecules. But of course, it was not so, and we did it all 'the hard way' as usual.

Gilbert Walton went on to comment on the apparent waste of the vital links between one generation of living creature and the next, namely seeds and spores and eggs, and here again he highlighted engineering lessons that we are only now beginning to learn, and *still* unaided by biological experience and observation:

The basic molecular material, called nucleic acid or 'DNA', does not appear to vary much from one organism to another. Combined in the nucleic acid is a limited number of amino acids, and the order in which they are linked appears to carry the complexity. The situation seems to be closely comparable to our own writing and printing which is used in the recipes for making things, whether it be in a cookery book for making a pudding, or in construction manuals for elaborate machinery. Here ink and paper are the basic materials which only vary in unimportant ways from one document to another. There are comparatively few letters in the alphabet, but the arrangement of these in sentences can carry an infinity of different instructions. In the same way there are comparatively few amino acids in the genetic material and it is believed that their arrangement forms the code which directs the multifarious growth of organisms and all their inherited characters.

The comparison between printing and genetic material may be carried further. It is often pointed out that nature is exceedingly wasteful. It is worth noticing, however, that the waste occurs in seeds and spores and eggs, and not in bulk organic and nitrogenous material which is carefully conserved in elaborate cyclic processes. Of all the acorns from an oak tree very few will grow into new trees, and of all the eggs from a fish few will hatch. It is a strange point that we ourselves waste paper and printing on a prodigious scale. We have only to think of the daily newspapers, the technical and trade journals, the advertising, let alone spoken words and talk. Certainly only a minute fraction of the paper printed, or the words spoken, is operative in creating new things or changing the structure of events, but like the tiny fraction of the seeds and spores that survives, it is an essential medium for what fruit there is.

In the origins of our language people must have appreciated the comparison between writing and seeds because the same words are used for both. Literature is disseminated, books are conceived, ideas germinate, plans hatch, and sermons are delivered. The parable of the sower has a double meaning; 'the seed is the word of God'.

It is only recently that we have come to learn that although aluminium is the third commonest element in the Earth's crust (after oxygen and silicon, and 8% of the whole) it is a very costly process, both in money and in energy, to extract it from the mineral bauxite. The fact is that we have probably now extracted as much metallic aluminium as we need for some time, provided we are prepared to recycle what we have already got, instead of allowing it to corrode away. Recycling, particularly of non-ferrous metals, has recently become fashionable, not of course through looking to biology but, to the everlasting shame of the engineer, through the pressures of the accountant!

THE CAUSE OF SHAPE

In another book on the subject of engineering and biology, still in course of preparation, I wrote:

One may subscribe to the belief that whilst topology is the theme that runs through the whole of the story of life and of engineering, this neither precludes the existence of an overall cause of, nor attempts to explain the reasons underlying the amazing variety of shapes both animate and inanimate. One (Schwenk, 1965) sees it all as the result of the two dominant fluids on earth, air and water. This puts it all in terms of the substances peculiar to our planet. Another man (D'Arcy Thompson, 1961) sees it as an elaborate extension of Euclidean geometry in three dimensions. Yet a third (Stevens, 1976) goes further and declares it to be the result of the limitations imposed by space itself, perhaps the nearest a man has ever come to putting the mysteries of Relativity and the quantities in which it deals, gravitation, inertia, electrostatics and electromagnetics, into physical ideas that most of us might be able to grasp.

One of the powerful aspects of this last approach is that it suggests a reason why absolute size may have a meaning, and is not therefore subject to the Principle of Relativity.

ADAPTABILITY

A study of natural creatures shows most emphatically that the secret of survival of almost every species has been its ability to adapt. As a schoolboy I caught the larva of a Puss moth, fully grown and about to pupate. Its normal habit is to climb a tree, gnaw off pieces of bark and chew them up to mix them with its own saliva which it then smears over its whole body, encapsulating itself in a synthetic bubble, stuck to the tree bark. The bubble itself being made from tree bark is therefore the perfect match and the most perfect piece of camouflage. Before I went to school I gave the caterpillar to my father to look after. All he knew was that caterpillars generally eat cabbage and pupate under the soil, so he put soil in a box, added some cabbage leaves and put fine netting over the top. By the time I returned from school the young Puss moth had nearly finished chewing up cabbage, mixing it with saliva and covering itself with the paste to stick it to the stem of a cabbage leaf. A local 'expert' was called in.

'Poor thing,' he declared, and told us what Puss moths really needed. 'The cabbage will putrefy and the larva will die, of course', he said. 'There is nothing you can do.' But the cabbage made into a paste, and the stalk to which it was attached, did *not* putrefy. Weeks later a healthy moth emerged, none the worse for having been raised in a quite foreign environment full of strange materials. But I think that had it not known the power of its saliva chemicals it would never have attempted the exercise, but gone on searching for a suitable substance until it died.

There are hundreds of similar stories of living creatures, including *Homo sapiens*, who have adapted to what would appear to outsiders as a totally hostile environment and one which is quite unique to them. Yet they all survived, and it is for this reason that one might deny Sir James Jeans his mathematician-like claim for the Almighty and declare 'God is an engineer'.

Some of the feats of birds are perhaps the most remarkable of all. A Wheatear makes the trip from Greenland to Spain in 48 hours and loses one half of its body weight in the process. The Arctic Tern flies from Alaska to Antarctica and back, making the round trip of over 40,000 miles in three months, an average speed of nearly 20 mph, and a Swift is thought to be capable of continuous flight for three years. In both of the latter cases, feeding is provided throughout the journey, by fish on the one hand and airborne insects on the other.

Owls can hit targets which are only illuminated by a candleflame at a distance of 1170 feet. A Golden Eagle can see an 18 inch target at two miles (a resolution of 0·0000025 of a degree of arc—or about $\frac{1}{100}$ second of arc).

Yet descend into the micro-organisms and there are wonders of adaptation even more remarkable. For example the marine bacterium *Leucothrix mucor* (a long filament in shape) reproduces by tying itself into a variety of knots that tighten more and more until the creature pinches itself into two or more pieces. Be assured, Nature has tried every trick in the book!

Now engineers must strive to be equally adaptable. There should be no 'energy crises', no 'world shortages' of this or that commodity. Engineers must be able to predict disasters in order to prevent them, to be always one step ahead, whether it be of their competitors or the general 'enemy'.

More than that, they must be adaptable as regards their specialist subject or even profession. I have known an electrical machine designer who began his career as a metallurgist, and a chemical engineer whose first degree was in electrical engineering. They will tell you that they are simply applying the same principles in new situations, but that takes a lot of experience and practice. Analogies, of course, always stand them in good stead, often better than the more formal laws of physics.

REFERENCES

D'Arcy Thompson, W. (1961) *On Growth and Form*. Cambridge, CUP

Lenihan, J. M. A. (1972) 'What is bio-engineering?' *Contemp. Phys.*, vol. 13, no. 3, pp. 295–309

Schwenk, T. (1965) *Sensitive Chaos*. London, Rudolf Steiner Press

Stevens, Peter S. (1976) *Patterns in Nature*. Harmondsworth, Penguin Books

Walton, G. (1964) 'Facts and artefacts', *Modern Churchman*, vol. VII, pp. 233–238

7

The Early Years

'Wisdom is the principal thing; therefore get wisdom:
And with all thy getting get understanding.'

(Proverbs, 4, vii)

During the late 1960s/early 1970s I had the honour to serve on
the Schools Science and Technology Committee, personally
set up and chaired by the Duke of Edinburgh, and in that role
saw the birth of engineering science in schools. There were
eleven of us in all, and I remember that after one meeting was
over formally, we began to discuss at what age children
make their choice between the sciences and the arts. We found
that we were all agreed that the basic, deep-rooted choice
is made, often subconsciously, between the ages of ten and
thirteen, and that having made the choice, only a small percentage ever swerve from it.

Of course, this does not mean that they have chosen to be
chemical engineer, metallurgist or aircraft designer at that
tender age although I *did* know a lad of thirteen who
announced that he wanted to be a geologist, and ten years
later he was indeed a fully qualified geologist. But such cases
are rare, and those who can do this are fortunate indeed. For
the vast majority, all they know is maths, physics, chemistry
and biology (if they are lucky enough to be allowed all four!).
In the 1930s physics in schools was largely taught like Latin—
as a discipline, and the main outlet at the end of a continuation
at university was to cram it into some other poor souls 'for
the good of their minds'. The situation is much better now.

Many schools have well-informed careers teachers. Local industry is at last waking up to the idea that it has long stood alone as the only commercial buyer who has had no say in the making of the product. So industrialists are beginning to woo the schools and make them aware that there are other things besides medicine, teaching and the Executive Civil Service exams that have their roots in physics.

So whilst it is true that, of all those doing 'O' levels in maths and physics, only *some* will finally become engineers, the reverse is quite different and virtually *all* engineers begin their careers, not so much with 'O' levels, but with 'A' levels in maths, physics, chemistry and (as I have said before), if they are lucky enough, biology. For 'A' level is almost the first occasion when they are allowed to make a selection of subjects of their own choosing and I find that sixth-formers of today have an altogether more mature outlook towards their chosen subjects than did my generation in its sixth-form days. It is almost as if many of them had already started their university undergraduate days, where you are learning because you *want* to, rather than *have* to. This of course is 90% of the way to success in any discipline. Having the will to learn means that you will stop at nothing to get the information you want. This is a most important possession at university (one might even call it a 'jewel') because whilst school teachers are all taught how to teach, university lecturers are not and the majority are bad at it. (One or two are so bad they have to be seen and heard to be believed!)

So the step from school to university can be very disturbing in that it is much more 'up to you' in the latter and the temptations of the new-found freedoms (being away from home, having 150 clubs in the Students' Union in which to enjoy yourself, drink, etc.) are the downfall of many. But it is comforting to see that engineers are generally less prone to failure from this 'disease' than students of many other disciplines, largely because there is so much to learn, including large slices of practical work which have to be written up, and engineering departments throughout the country have a habit of giving their undergraduates (especially first-years) a pretty tight schedule of formal lectures and labs, which has the effect of keeping most of them immune to what the old song used to call: 'The Sir John Barleycorn, nicotine and the temptations of Eve!' This is not to say that undergraduate life, even as an engineer, is one long slog. If you don't enjoy yourself in three years as an undergraduate I reckon you never will!

As you progress through first and second years you get an opportunity to look at where you are heading, and where some of your colleagues are heading, and maybe you begin to wonder if your choice has been right for you. University departments are quite sympathetic to such situations and within limits, and depending on which university is involved, 'deflections' at least are possible. (One is mentioned on p. 149) in which a final-year physics undergraduate was allowed to spend the entire third year in the electrical engineering department.)

As final year begins (in a three-year course) you will be made aware that either postgraduate work or employment is only a few months away. By January or February the firms are sending representatives to universities to interview students who so wish, with a view to offering them jobs conditional on getting a certain class of degree in finals. Even this is not always insisted upon, and I remember making a plea with a well-known firm on behalf of a third-year student who failed his finals so badly that he did not get even a Pass degree. The firm took my word and employed him. Two years later when the interviewer came around again he asked if we had any more students like John X—said he was just what they needed. I had known that the reason he had failed was that he had spent nearly all of his third year running the Students' Union and he was a brilliant organiser. A brilliant organiser with just a superficial knowledge of engineering is excellent for many posts in industry—advertising, for example.

Even before the interviews engineering students are encouraged to sample industry, or the scientific Civil Service, by working for eight weeks of their long vacations, after first and second years are over each July, with a firm or in a government establishment. The pay is not marvellous and a student can get a much more lucrative job selling carpets in the multiple store near home, or better still taking seaside snapshots for holidaymakers on the beach, but this can easily be the top of a slippery slope, and the dedicated student will welcome the opportunity to have a look at real engineering life. Often, the vacation jobs are followed by offer of employment and the new graduate returns to the firm where eight weeks that he or she enjoyed were spent two years earlier as first-year students.

SANDWICH COURSES

Now what I have just described is the (almost old-fashioned, some might say) straight from school–to university–to job approach. But there are several alternatives. One of the lessons that was learned after World War II was that people benefit more from university courses if they are a little older than normal school-leaving age. The average age of the first-year electricals at Manchester in 1946 was twenty-six, and over one third of the intake got 1st class Honours. When National Service was still in force in the 1950s students who opted to do their service *before* taking their degree generally did better than those who took their degree straight from school. The nature of their activity during National Service could hardly be called 'academic', so it seemed to matter little how the two years were occupied. It was just the fact that they were two years older that was important.

Now couple with this the recognition by industry that if you support students financially, not only are you likely to implant a feeling of indebtedness, however subconscious, but the students are more likely to become accustomed to your methods and less likely to risk a change when it comes to job-choosing time. Some, of course, will take the money and walk away to join some other firm at the end of the degree course. Others may leave the firm soon after employment. However firm a contract you make with a student to the effect that he *must* work for x years for you *after* graduating, no firm wants an unwilling employee, and provided most of the big firms act alike they will gain and lose the people who have been supported and on average the losses will equal the gains, so everybody benefits.

It only took a short time (perhaps days!) before the idea of a school-leaver working for a period in industry, then going to university, then returning to the same firm for a specified minimum period was given the name 'sandwich course'. One feels that the name must have come from an academic because, as everyone knows, the interesting part of a sandwich is the middle! Be that as it may, the sandwiches were soon to be divided into 'thick' and 'thin' varieties.

In a thick sandwich the student leaves school to join a firm for one year. This is followed by a full three- or four-year degree course, with industrial training in the long vacations and a final year in industry.

Also known as a 'thick' sandwich (although I would have called it a double-decker/open sandwich to follow the food analogy through precisely) is an arrangement whereby the student begins with two years at a university/polytechnic followed by one year in industry, before completing the final year of the degree course, and following it with a further year of industrial training.

The thin sandwich is a multiple decker, being a four-year degree course with alternate six-month periods in industry and education. In most cases a further six months in industry is required after the degree is awarded.

A further type of industrial commitment, known as an 'integrated' course, involves a short pre-university industrial course, with industrial periods of ten weeks in each of the three or four academic years. This is only a minimal extension on the old-fashioned straight university course with vacation attachments, except that it is formalised, with the freedom to change firms removed and an industrial period before and after written in.

However, these courses can be either industry-based or college-based. In an industry-based course the sponsoring company undertakes to provide all the industrial training needed to meet the professional Institution requirements. In a college-based course the university or polytechnic arranges the periods of training which allow the student to go to different companies, and there is no formal link between the student and any one company. The onus is on the student in this case to ensure that all the training adds up to a qualifying amount for the appropriate professional Institution.

A list of sponsoring firms and their requirements is published annually on behalf of the Institutions of Electrical, Mechanical and Production Engineers. The 1983 list includes 64 sponsoring organisations and to emphasise the variety within the profession, discussed in Chapter 5, the list includes both nationalised and private industry, including:

Austin Rover Group	GEC
British Aerospace	ICI
The BBC	Marconi Radar Systems
British Rail	Michelin Tyres
British Shipbuilding	Ministry of Defence
Cadbury Schweppes	National Coal Board
Chubb and Sons Lock and Safe Co.	Pilkington Glass
	Shell UK
Co-operative Wholesale Society	Thorn EMI Electronics
Ferranti	Westland Helicopters

Consideration of the various types of job that are available in every *one* of the above list gives perhaps a better indication of the 'many faces of engineering' than anything I have written in the chapter of that title.

What industry has to gain from sponsorship is first pick of a batch of students who are already knowledgeable about the industry when they graduate. Industry hopes they will be better engineers, too, for having had the experience. What the students have to gain is being paid more than the standard grant whilst they are learning.

AIMING LOWER

So far in this chapter I have assumed that the reader might be interested in going all the way to becoming a chartered engineer, which involves at least a first degree or its

104

equivalent as educational requirement. But for those who want to make 'things' more than they want to make 'decisions', or who think they cannot cope with three years of high-level maths, or the like, there are just as interesting careers at technician engineer or technician level.

The very early years follow the same pattern as those described in the early part of this chapter, as far as 'O' levels. From this point the technician engineer needs to be qualified educationally by obtaining a Higher National Diploma in the appropriate subject of his choice, or a Technician Education Council Higher Certificate or Diploma (in Scotland, a Scottish Education Council equivalent). After that he needs five years of industrial experience of which two must be spent on a training scheme. He is then qualified as a technician engineer, and can be a member of his own Institution, run along similar lines to the Institutions of the Chartered Engineers.

I have lectured many times at meetings of branches of both kinds of Institution and have found it difficult to differentiate between the two kinds of audience, judging from the discussions, both formal and informal, which have followed. An Institution is a club, whatever else it is, where people meet to enjoy themselves and be entertained, as well as improving their knowledge occasionally.

A technician's qualification is an Ordinary National Diploma or a Technician Education Council (Scottish Technical Education Council in Scotland) certificate or diploma, together with at least two years practical training and not less than two years experience.

THE PROFESSIONAL INSTITUTIONS

It is particularly important during the early years to become familiar with the position and role of the institutions that are associated with, and to a large extent 'run', the professions. Unlike the medical, legal and architectural professions, the engineering organisations are not so tightly sewn up that no one outside can practise. But there are certain limits. Anyone, for example, can fit new wiring to their houses, add new lights and power points, and so on, *but they cannot, by law, connect them to the existing mains supply*. Only a chartered electrical engineer can do that and then only after testing and finding that the new installation conforms to the standards and regulations laid down by the Institution at that time. So one role of the Institutions is to act as watchdog to make sure that engineering standards, particularly those concerned with *safety*, are being maintained.

Another obvious role of the professional bodies is to set the academic and training standards needed for the award of the various grades of membership, the most important of which is that of full member when the recipient becomes a chartered engineer and is entitled to write 'C.Eng.' after his or her name. It is as high a qualification as that of the general practitioner in medicine, who in addition to the letters 'M.B., Ch.B.' has a certificate authorising the practice of medicine and surgery. The chartered engineer has a similar certificate. Many of the Institutions are proud of the fact that they themselves have a Royal Charter as approval of their organisation.

Another most important aspect of the Institution is the dissemination of knowledge through the writing and publication of learned papers, some of which are read and discussed at meetings, both at the headquarters and at regional and local centres. The discussions may also be published. Naturally, as with any national organisation, an Institution is divided geographically into regions and the regions are often further divided into districts. Each region has its own committee, which may carry as many as thirty members or more, and has representation from the lower grades of the profession, as well as the chartered members. The younger members often run their own committees, organise meetings, visits, etc.

The headquarters has its organisation divided into main boards on which representatives from the regional committees serve. There may also be members of a board serving in their own right. Above the boards is a council, the 'law-giver', comprising the chairmen of the boards and senior engineers elected from the members by ballot. The organisation is totally democratic. Any member can be proposed for election to a board or to council by nomination by a specified number of other members. Advertising is more than frowned upon, and those whose responsibility is to serve on a board or on council do so in their own right, and *not* as representatives of GEC or whichever firm happens to employ them.

But when all these activities have been studied and amplified, there is more, much more, to being a member of a professional institution.

When you join, even as a student member, you have joined a club, as you might join the local badminton or tennis club, because you are interested in the subject on which the club is based. You want to meet others of like interest, not only to play the game but to join in a social life in which marriage partners are catered for and encouraged to come to the various activities.

Above all perhaps, there is a sense of *belonging*—belonging to a group of fellow humans of like interests, of having the opportunity to have a hand in running the business, of having extra security in your job, for most of the Institutions have an organisation that looks after those members who fall on hard times financially. There are travel grants for younger members and many other benefits that cannot even be listed as hard cash.

A young man who once shared an office with me back in the 1950s refused to join the Institution on the grounds that, 'I can do everything that I could do as a member of the IEE—write and submit papers for publication in the Proceedings, have the papers read at the headquarters and at regional centres, be awarded premiums (prizes) for my papers—and all without paying a penny in membership subscriptions' (which are not exactly cheap). 'What else is there?' he would ask me derisively. I would try to tell him that the 'other things' resembled the intangible benefits of marriage and friendship, where what you put *into* it rather than what you got *out* of it, brought its own rewards. He was not convinced by my arguments. But I noted with satisfaction, some years later, that he had not only joined the IEE, but become a chartered electrical engineer even though, like myself, he stayed an academic. It could be argued, you see, that academics have their own university or college as 'club' with all its attendant social life, etc. But still the professional club has something else to offer, and remember that there is no compulsion to join and that you can resign whenever you like. But a glance at the new member list and the resignation list each month will be indication itself as to whether those who have joined think it worthwhile!

THE OVERALL PICTURE

Like any healthy organisation, a professional institution is constantly changing its rules, updating its required standards and keeping a watchful eye on what goes on in other countries. An electrical engineer of fifty years ago might throw up his hands in horror to see that new vacuum cleaners are now connected to the mains by only two wires. The third, 'earthed' wire, the very lifeline of safety, has been removed! This is the result not only of vast improvements in insulation techniques but of the recognition of such by the profession, and in this particular case by the counterparts of the UK Institution of Electrical Engineers in Europe, for it was the presence of the EEC that accelerated the move to the two-wire connection in the UK. A similar exercise took place in relation to the colour coding of wiring.

Just as there are professional institutions of electrical engineers in many countries, so the UK Institution of Electrical Engineers has regional centres in many countries. It all adds to the communication between peoples, which is so vitally important in these days.

And this is only *one* profession. In each country there are roughly the same number of other professional bodies. In the UK these were managed under a single organisation, the Council of Engineering Institutions (CEI) which also had a Royal Charter granted in 1965. Being by comparison with the older Institutions of Civil, Mechanical and Electrical Engineers, a relative newcomer, it was much more in a state of flux than were those of the long-established professions and the membership (by institutions, that is) of the CEI was constantly changing.

In 1977 a committee was appointed under the chairmanship of Sir Monty Finniston to look again at the whole engineering structure and its findings were published in a report (*Engineering our Future*, 1980) which became known as the Finniston Report. Its recommendations included a proposal for a new Engineering Council (EC) to be established under a Royal Charter which assumed that the new body would in due course take over CEI's powers to maintain a register of engineers and to award titles to registrants. In October 1981 the CEI board publicly confirmed its willingness to seek the agreement of the membership (which includes all 200,000 chartered engineers) to this transfer when it was satisfied that their interests would be fully protected under the new arrangements.

In June 1982 the Engineering Council asked the CEI to take early steps to transfer these powers to them, but the CEI sought further clarification and there followed many meetings and exchanges of letters. By 30 September the EC had issued a Policy Statement, although discussions still continued, but on 11 November 1982 the CEI board met and decided by the required two-thirds majority to transfer the relevant powers. Now it was the turn of the individual members (the chartered engineers themselves) to give it their individual confirmation, and forms were circulated to allow all to vote.

Late in 1983 it was clear that the overall answer was 'YES', so the process of transfer was by no means an instantaneous affair and the exact date of take-over was not known at the time this book was being written. The remainder of this chapter is therefore being written as the situation was under CEI in November 1982. In this way I am sure that I understand what I am writing. For the rest, I can assure you that the change to EC will be seen as progress (200,000 members can hardly be wrong!) and many of the differences are of such subtlety that they will escape you until you are well established in the profession, by which time the change-over will be just a part of the history of a healthy organisation which is, of necessity, ever changing to keep pace with the advances of the front runners.

The list of CEI Corporation Members as of November 1982 runs as follows:

Royal Aeronautical Society
Institution of Chemical Engineers
Institution of Civil Engineers
Institution of Electrical Engineers
Institution of Electronic and Radio Engineers
Institute of Energy
Institution of Gas Engineers
Institution of Marine Engineers
Institution of Mechanical Engineers
Institution of Metallurgists
Institution of Mining Engineers
Institution of Mining and Metallurgy
Institution of Municipal Engineers
Royal Institution of Naval Architects
Institution of Production Engineers
Institution of Structural Engineers

—a total of sixteen bodies in all.

In addition, there are a number of affiliated bodies listed as follows:

Association of Mining Electrical and Mechanical
    Engineers
Biological Engineering Society
British Institute of Non-destructive Testing
Institute of Hospital Engineering
Institution of Agricultural Engineers
Institution of Highways and Transportation
Institution of Nuclear Engineers
Institution of Plant Engineers
Institution of Public Health Engineers
Institution of Public Lighting Engineers
North East Coast Institution of Engineers and
    Shipbuilders
Welding Institute

Examination of this list shows that nearly all could be said to be 'hybrids' of the corporation bodies proper. They are concerned with the professions that cut across the disciplines and, unless I am vitally mistaken, they are likely to increase their numbers and become dominant as the explosion of knowledge continues. In the next century a man or woman will be an 'engineer' again, just as they were a century ago. The 'Corporation Engineering Institutions' of 1982 may well have become lost in a mass of healthy overgrowth, just as an untended garden will soon lose its geometrical flower beds, rows of the same species of plant, etc. This does not mean a return to chaos and anarchy. It represents the true progress towards a better future and you, the young engineers joining today, will have a great part to play in shaping that future. There *is* such a thing as an 'organised chaos', and where you find it you tend to find it in an exceedingly healthy society.

In the Technician Engineer Section, the Engineers Registration Board of the CEI listed (in 1982) 45 organisations. Only a sample will be given here to give some idea of the scope and diversity of these:

> Association of Water Officers
> Bureau of Engineer Surveyors
> Chartered Institution of Building Services
> Institute of Automotive Engineer Assessors
> Institute of Measurement and Control
> Institute of the Motor Industry
> Institute of Quality Assurance
> Institute of Sheet Metal Engineering
> Royal Aeronautical Society
> Society of Licensed Aircraft Engineers and
>   Technologists
> Society of X-ray Technology

In addition, almost all the corporation member institutions and affiliates have their counterpart organisations in this list.

In the Engineering Technician Section the skilled craftsmen and women are much in evidence in the 34 bodies in the 1982 list, which includes:

Institute of Marine Engineers
Institute of Metallurgical Technicians
Institute of Plumbing
Institute of Road Transport Engineers, etc.

WHAT KINDS OF PEOPLE GO INTO ENGINEERING?

There are several single-sentence answers that one might give to such a question, none of which is particularly informative without amplification. For example:

'Those who want to improve the quality of life.'

Such an answer could also be given to the question, 'What kind of people make good missionaries?' So let us try again:

'Those who are interested in utilising the world's resources to best advantage for mankind.'

—a better attempt, but still too high-minded. Let's get down to the more personal and immediate problems of choosing a career, and answer:

'Those who want job satisfaction at reasonable pay.'

But this applies to librarians, actors and actresses (if they are good at it); footballers likewise. One could go on supplying one-sentence answers like these without ever really describing what engineers are like.

So let me tackle the problem in a different way. I meet and converse with tens of thousands of people in the course of a year. Many of them are engineers. Often I can tell from one or two sentences which members of a group of people are engineers of one kind or another. So let me put myself on the spot and ask myself, 'How can I tell?'

Perhaps the first noticeable characteristic is that of applying common sense *first* to any new problem or situation. If someone in a public house switched on a TV set to watch the news and neither picture nor sound emerged, it is highly probable in my experience that an engineer would be the first to ask, 'Is it plugged in?' even before he began banging the set with

112

his hand! But a more contrived example, and one which therefore you are more likely to remember, is that of a problem set by a stranger in a country pub to four men seated at the same table one lunch-time and joined by our self-styled quiz-master. The latter rapidly discovers that one of the four is a physicist, one a chemist and one an engineer, but he fails to discover the profession of the fourth man. However, he issues each with the same challenge. 'I have here four barometers of the old-fashioned mercury-in-glass type. I propose to give one to each of the four of you and during the course of the afternoon you are to use it to determine the height of the local church tower in the village. I offer a substantial reward for the most nearly correct answer, already known to me.'

All four accepted the challenge. They drew lots as to the order in which they would conduct their experiments, knowing that otherwise, spying on each other would bring unpleasantness and 'There is really no reason why the other three should not watch the man performing', said the quiz master.

The chemist was drawn first. He remembered from his school days of thirty years ago that barometric pressure varied with height, so he took his barometer and climbed the church tower. At the top he read the barometer, then climbed down and read it again. It read the same! (Victorian-vintage barometers have a habit of doing that.) So he knocked the glass—a common thing to do—then it read differently, so he noted the difference and from it did a calculation, after much memory-searching, which led him to the conclusion that the tower was 32,521 feet high. He knew that this could not possibly be correct, but he could not see any better way of using the crude apparatus he had been given, nor how his competitors might do better, except by luck, so he submitted this as his answer.

Now it was the turn of the physicist. He had been doing some thinking, thinking what the crude engineer might do. There *were* other ways of using a barometer after all. He too climbed the tower, carrying his barometer to the top. The others noticed that he then consulted his watch which had a seconds hand, as well as the usual minute and hour hands. He then dropped the barometer over the side and timed it until it reached the ground, contemplated using relativity for the time the light signal of the crash took to reach his eye and dismissed it as insignificant. The watch was the least accurate measuring device so he simply used the formula $h = \frac{1}{2} gt^2$ and worked out the height as 93·14 metres, which the quiz master had to convert to 305·81 feet to compare with the answers of the other competitors and what was more important, with the answer in the parish records!

Then came the engineer who considered that the physicist had cheated because he had used additional apparatus in the form of a timing device and not merely the barometer itself. 'If that is within the rules,' he thought, 'I can be much more accurate using additional apparatus, for the barometer only took just over 4 seconds to fall, and he could not be more accurate than $\pm\frac{1}{5}$ second using an ordinary wrist watch, so he could easly be 5% out.' So the engineer went into a shop and bought a ball of string, and a tape measure, took both string and barometer to the top of the tower. He tied one end of the string to the barometer and lowered it over the side until its lower end just touched the ground. Then he cut off the string level with the top of the tower. He then went down to the ground and carefully measured the string, made a separate experiment with a shorter but known length of string to measure how much it stretched under the weight of the barometer, even contemplated taking the total weight of string into consideration in a calculus integration, and emerged with the answer, 'The tower is 297 feet 9½ inches which I round off to 298 feet.'

The fourth man, having observed all this, set out away from the church carrying his barometer. An hour later he returned without the barometer and declared, never having been near the tower, that 'the height of the tower is 298 feet 1¾ inches'. 'That is exactly right!' exclaimed the questioner. 'But how on earth did you find out?' Simple,' said the contestant, 'I asked the verger.' 'But you didn't use the barometer!' shouted the other three almost in unison. 'Oh yes I did', he said. 'The verger was having his tea and it took a lot of persuasion to get him to leave it and go and look up the height in the parish records. I gave him the barometer as final incentive to go.' 'May I ask now, sir,' said the quiz-master, 'what *is* your profession?' 'I am a door-to-door salesman', was the flat reply!

This story may tell you more about door-to-door salesmen than it does about the others, but it does also tell you a great deal about engineers. Spare a thought for the chemist, he did have to go first and was misled into thinking that he must *only* use the barometer (which also, incidentally, the salesman did!).

No, the engineering profession is not full of 'wide boys' ready to make a 'quick buck'; in fact, in general, a quick buck is the last thing you are likely to make, unless you are extremely fortunate. You are a person who believes that you will get out rewards in proportion to the effort you put in. You are also a person who reasons this way:

'I am awake perhaps 16 or 17 hours a day. I shall spend over half that time at my job. If I do not get on well with other people, or like the work, or get satisfaction from being on a winning team, I shall, by and large, be unhappy for more than half my waking life!'

The vast majority of the engineers that I know are basically *happy* people. I am sure that one of the contributory factors to this is the ability to change one's kind of work—kind of life, without ever leaving the profession. Their happiness is marked by a sense of humour. A person who can invent a new device, or improve a process, can also think of original remarks in new situations and particularly if they bring a grin to the faces of colleagues.

Engineers take their jobs seriously, but rarely so seriously that they become dull, stodgy people incapable of talking about anything but their work. They rarely get fanatical about world issues even though they are ready to discuss them. Some have been known to get fanatical about ferrets or even collecting butterflies, but they are generally good company and rarely mean-minded because 'the job's the thing'. In this they have much in common with the acting profession where the sentiment 'The show goes on' is legendary. A number of engineers I know are often accused of being 'married to their job'. It is possible—it is always possible. But like any other collection of humans, 'It takes all kinds!' Among the bad features not often found among engineers is loneliness—the very nature of the job precludes it. Again there have been exceptions, and the history of Oliver Heaviside makes fascinating reading for engineer and non-engineer alike. Among the good qualities I have rarely found a designer who is resentful, or bears malice or is deceitful. Argue? They argue like mad, about all sorts of things, from the colour of the paint to company policy, but generally without losing temper or quarrelling. What is science, after all, if it is not argument, and there has to be a good deal of science in every engineer. Nor am I trying to create an image of a profession filled with humans little lower than the angels. There is competitiveness only to be compared with that on a football field, which can descend to such things as industrial espionage, but it is generally of collective origin and does not usually reflect the personality of the run-of-the-mill engineer.

It is only when you reach the real 'corridors of power' that greed and other undesirable characteristics, of which most of us are capable, are liable to be allowed to surface. But this, happily, is not an immediate concern in 'The Early Years'.

REFERENCE

Engineering our Future (1980), Report of the Committee of Inquiry into the Engineering Profession, Cmnd 7794. London, HMSO

8

The Daily Round

'The trivial round, the common task,
Will furnish all we need to ask'
(*John Keble, Hymns A&M*)

THE PROFESSIONAL MAN

In the early days of television in the UK, before commercial
television appeared, the strictest watch was kept on any kind
of advertising that the unscrupulous might like to slip into
a comedian's joke. Since a lot of the programmes went out
'live' there was always, of course, the chance of a genuine slip
of the tongue such as, 'I was just Hoovering the carpet', when
'vacuuming' was intended.

Some professions are completely banned from advertising,
the most notable of which is the medical profession, with the
legal and architectural professions a good second and third.
This rule was followed in the new medium to the extent that
a general practitioner, who happened to be eye witness to
a bank robbery and was therefore being interviewed by a
reporter for television, was never to say, 'I am a doctor', even
though the reason he was on the screen had nothing whatever
to do with his profession. The situation reached its climax
perhaps in panel games which were, after all, purely-for-fun,
family viewing. A team of three people might be introduced
as: 'Mr Smith is a greengrocer, Miss Johnson is a hairdresser
and Mr Robinson is a *professional* man.' This 'professional

man' turned up so often that those of us who were also 'professional men' (like mechanical engineers or metallurgists) wanted to throw things at the TV set every time it happened. We all knew that the man in question was either a medic or a lawyer or an architect, by comparison with which the rest of us were rubbish!

What was fact was that those three professions had the rules of their respective institutions drawn up so tightly that the best of trade unions might have envied them. In particular no one unqualified could practise at all, let alone call himself an architect or whatever. Imagine an engineering institution so exclusive that no garage mechanic is allowed to touch a screwdriver!

Some of us have managed to go a part of the way, and no one but a chartered electrical engineer may install new apparatus in a private house and connect it to the public electricity supply. Others do, and 99% get away with it, but legally they can be prosecuted for doing so. One of the wiring regulations that put virtually 100% of homes legally liable to disconnection was 'Flexible leads shall be visible along their entire length.' About the only way to live with such a regulation is to take all 'flexes' straight up to the ceiling and make a sort of spider's web across the ceiling area, and which of us is prepared to do that?

So the more free-and-easy attitude persists among the engineering profession, but that does not mean that the individual members are any less dedicated than those of the medical, dental or legal professions, nor even those disgustingly underpaid members of the nursing and teaching professions which are possibly the most important in the country.

THE CRYSTAL BALL

I say possibly, because it is not difficult to argue that the engineering professions are the most important of all. It only needs an electricians' strike, or the amazing situation that occurred once in February 1974 when miners were picketing the power stations, for most of the country to grind to near standstill—and yet—*essential* services, hospitals, establishments affecting national defence, and the like were kept supplied. How was that done? The answer is by the engineers doing the jobs of the electricians, with or without the latter's approval. But suppose the situation were to be reversed and the Institution of Electrical Engineers called for all its members to stop work. The country could not survive for a week. Electricians could not do the job that the engineers do, and black-out would be *total*!

I mention all this because the engineering profession, like the 'sacred' professions of early TV days, is not one that people tend to enter and leave in the way that a person might have a variety of jobs such as insurance clerk, commercial traveller, store detective, sports writer and publican, all within the space of ten years. An engineer, having persevered through all the years of technical education, practical training and experience-gathering, tends to stay with the profession until retirement although the emphasis might shift from time to time. I have known engineers so versatile that it was difficult to know in which branch they took their first degree, but they were never outside the profession as a whole.

It seemed appropriate therefore to devote a chapter to describing the kind of life one might look forward to by the age of 40 or 50, even though there will inevitably be a considerable amount of 'crystal ball' gazing used in the process. For, like other professions, the ups and downs of one's career are bound to be affected by the state of the nation, the state of the world, major wars, etc., and no one can predict such factors with any accuracy at all.

When I was a new graduate in 1949 the 'safe' thing to do was to join a large reputable firm such as the Metropolitan–Vickers Electrical Co. Ltd, where one could look forward to steady progress, or accelerated progress, depending on how much personal ability one had and how much effort one was prepared to put into the job. The 'adventurous' thing to do was to become an academic, where a three-year appointment with absolutely no promises at the end was the very best the new graduate could be offered. If lucky, this could be followed by a Lectureship, but then only on probation for three years, with the possibility of dismissal without explanation at the end of it. After permanent appointment, six years beyond graduation, there was a merit bar on pay increments, and only if one reached those dizzy heights of Senior Lecturer could one start living, as opposed to 'existing', by drawing a salary comparable with the graduate who had opted for industry and served only a couple of years or so.

The phrase was coined in university circles, 'Ah, for the peace and quiet of industry!' Who could have foretold that within twenty years Metropolitan–Vickers would have merged with British Thomson Houston to make Associated Electrical Industries who then, together with English Electric —another 'safe' giant—would have been swallowed up by the General Electric Company, with redundancies and 'golden handshakes' at almost all levels. In the second half of that same period came a huge expansion programme in academic establishments. Colleges of advanced technology ('CATs') were upgraded to university status, which delighted all heads of departments in those establishments who became entitled to the rank of Professor overnight. Whole new universities sprang up like mushrooms: Lancaster, York, Kent, Essex, Sussex, Surrey and others. Any new graduate with flair could get an assistant lecturer's job for the asking, with virtual guarantee of permanent appointment to follow. Several reached the grade of Professor in their early thirties. Where now 'the peace and quiet of industry'? Then came the world recession in the 1970s and the universities were hit, especially the new ones and the upgraded CATs—and so the pendulum swings. Who would be so bold as to forecast the 'safe' place for the new graduate of the 1980s?

And yet, one factor stands out above even national and international fortunes—a *good* engineer will always be able to command a good job—will always be needed. For they are the salt of the earth! One reads in times of depression of 'university graduates who are unemployed'; but the newspaper reporter forgets to say that they were not engineering graduates, or if they were, they had 3rd class Honours or Pass degrees. An engineer with a 1st class Honours degree seldom goes many days without a job.

The Daily Round

One of the things that is bound to worry a sixth-former considering the engineering profession is: 'Just what am I letting myself in for? I have read that university courses are more tightly scheduled than most, that I shall not be a qualified engineer for at least seven years, which involves having risen to a "position of responsibility" after five years, and that it is a career for life, a career about which I know very little. After all, my careers teacher is not an engineer and can only read leaflets, as I can. There are of course the occasional visits by engineers but they by no means cover the whole range of branches of the subject.'

This is a question that I feel no one can answer completely. It is a fact that there are so many and varied branches of engineering and so many different ways of life in each branch that nothing short of an encyclopaedia would be needed to give a complete picture, and who would have the time or patience to read it?

Perhaps the best way to allay some of the fears is to point out how academic establishments are making it possible to delay choices for as long as possible, in order to give you time to get to know fellow undergraduates at university who are planning careers different from yours, and if you ever find yourself saying 'I wish I'd done that', to give you time to do something about it and change course.

It was to this end that a number of universities offered engineering science as a full degree course in which a wide variety of courses is offered in first and second years and specialisation is reserved for third year when you ought to be in a better position to know what interests you most—be it the job itself, the immediate pay, the prospects of promotion, or wherever you wish to place the emphasis. Even in more formal departments where you 'sign on' specifically for 'civil engineering' or 'aeronautical engineering', you will find more courses of lectures available than you will need to attend in order to obtain full marks in the necessary number of examination papers you must sit over the three- or four-year course.

121

In a number of universities there is a common first-year course for all civil, mechanical, electrical and aeronautical engineering, and if you find that you might have opted for the wrong course, or *even if your examination marks in the first year suggest it*, transfer from one of these four courses to another is rare, but not unknown, depending of course on the university in question.

Remember that a personal tutor will always be there to advise you on all matters. What is more, you will find that as the years progress the choice gets wider, as it must. An electrical engineering department, for example, may strive to offer a complete range of courses so that a final-year student may choose only those courses relevant to a future career in one of the following:

> Computer engineering
> Electronics
> Power electronics
> Electrical machines
> Power systems
> Telecommunications
> Control systems including robotics
> and other major topics

It is very necessary that this be so, principally because you will be two years older before you have to choose and age, by itself, is a very important factor, as already discussed on pp. 99–100.

If your aim is then to get a 1st class Honours degree and pursue postgraduate research for a time (not necessarily a lifetime as an academic, but perhaps to obtain a Ph.D. after three years) then you will have had time to look at your own department and see just who among the staff (if any) is doing the kind of research you consider exciting, to note whether or not he is taking an active interest in having you join him. If not, there are booklets containing a synopsis of all research in British university departments and you can choose to make a move after graduating.

You can also be interviewed by representatives from industrial firms to find out how they personally value an engineer with a Ph.D. as opposed to a first degree only, for some make no distinction between the two, whilst others value the extra age and experience highly.

Again, with a first degree in the bag, it is possible to make a quite violent change in direction if you propose to change university to do a Ph.D. You might, for example, have a degree in mechanical engineering and opt for a Ph.D. in psychology at another university with a view to becoming an industrial psychologist. Nor will your first degree have been wasted if you eventually do this. It will always be there in the background to give you a better idea of the workings of the minds of the people who are then basically your 'patients'.

If the history of the subject begins to fascinate you as your undergraduate course progresses you may wish to investigate the kind of work that might be offered to you as an industrial archaeologist, a subject unknown half a century ago.

ENTERING INDUSTRY

Nor does the freedom of choice end with the change from academic learning to taking up employment. You may have specialised in electronics in your final year and therefore accepted a job with an electronics firm, but you are in no way committed to becoming a project leader in the manufacture of a particular component. Do you think the head of sales in that firm attended any courses in salesmanship in his student days? (He *does* have a degree, although actually it was in metallurgy!)

At this stage you should never forget that you went to university to have your *mind trained*, and that no matter how much universities lean over in the 1980s to industrialise their courses so as to make the transition from university to firm as smooth as possible, it will finally be the firm who employs you who educates you in their methods, offers you the opportunity for change of way of life, still within their organisation, and the freedom of choice is always there. A fellow graduate of my year effectively became a journalist—an engineering journalist that is—and eventually became technical editor of the journal *Flight*. (His first degree was in physics!)

Now perhaps I am in a better position to answer the question with which I began this discussion under the heading 'Freedom of choice'. If you do 'A' levels with a view to doing an engineering degree at university or polytechnic, you are scarcely committing yourself in any way in regard to what your future daily life will be like. It is not anything so vital a decision as those of emigrating, getting married, having children, moving house or other similar facets of life that constitute the real 'crossroads'.

If you like travel, you can be an engineer in almost any branch of the subject and have a most profitable career with all the travel you want. If you are mathematically inclined, both industrial and academic worlds will receive you with open arms. If your inclinations are virtually the opposite, you are still equally welcome, although many (academics in particular) will give you the impression that this is not so. The Professor of my own student days, the late Sir Frederic Williams, developed the world's first full-scale computer in 1951 and often boasted that throughout his career he had never had occasion to integrate anything more complicated than $\sin \theta$! But he was a master of delegation, which one of his staff summarised by saying that his staff consisted of 'E.S.s' and 'M.S.s'—experimental slaves and mathematical slaves. I am honoured to have been one of the E.S.s and I'm quite sure by subsequent career owed much of its success to that kind of training. Really good delegators in industry are a boon to any firm, but it is almost something built into our personality rather than something that can be formalised and taught. So study yourself, decide whether you like people or whether you like machines. Decide when you are happiest (when not at home or with friends, that is) and try to direct your career accordingly.

THE FULL LIFE

Engineering is a full life, and a very rewarding life. It invades so many other professions as diverse as journalism, farming, the Armed Services and the medical profession.

It is as well rewarded, financially, as you want it to be and are prepared to work for. In that respect it is not unlike the Caucus-race in *Alice in Wonderland*. You can begin running when you like and leave off when you like. You can largely shape the kind of daily life you will be having by the time you are fifty, despite the strange twists of fate and the crystal ball.

If safety of tenure is your aim then I can pass on to you the advice that was given to me on graduation. 'If you have any inclination towards the "heavy" side of the business (machines and power systems) then stay with it, for there will always be a need to generate more and more electricity and therefore a need for people to know how to do it.' But that was 1949, and what was true of machines and power at that time is now equally true of the 'light' side of the business. There will always be TV sets, computers, microprocessors and many other devices that have come to stay, and there will always be the need for real experts in these subjects.

A SPECIFIC EXAMPLE

Let us take just one facet of the profession where an engineer can get almost as far away from the whims of the crystal ball as possible. I refer to the national electricity supply organisation in the UK, at present a nationalised industry run by the Central Electricity Generating Board. This is unlikely ever to become a British Rail type of industry where it gets into the hands of master accountants who decide that making profit is more important than giving a service, and that 'streamlining' (shutting down more and more lines that do not pay their way), is a necessary evolution for the industry (rather like the passing of the Dinosaurs, one feels).

On the contrary all the evidence suggests that more and more electricity will be needed as the next century approaches, and that the system will become more and more complex. The only major upheaval one could possibly see would be sub-division of the system into inter-connected regions, which would lead to a need for *more* new technology and *more* jobs, not fewer.

The fact that jobs with the CEGB are 'safe' is in no way a suggestion that they are dull. There are dull jobs within the American Space Organisation. In any case, what is a dull job for one person is exciting for another. A large part of contentment in an occupation is in fitting your personality to the kind of task required. As with almost any large organisation, the variety of tasks for engineers and the possibilities for transfer within the organisation allow you to do this. Never imagine that the generation of electricity only needs electrical engineers. There are physicists and chemists, micro-biologists, marine biologists, metallurgists and almost every other kind of engineer in the generating business.

The CEGB has 20 million customers whom it supplies from over one hundred power stations. About 25% of its staff are professionally qualified engineers or equally qualified pure scientists. The Board itself points out that job satisfaction comes from an awareness that one is employed in a public service fundamental to the national economy and prosperity. You would not be forging weapons of war. Your work would be as vital to the sick as that of the surgeon, the work itself no less interesting.

Their graduate training scheme illustrates what I said earlier about the university training your mind but the employer teaching you the job. The CEGB's training scheme is designed to provide two distinct types of professional engineer: one aiming to progress to management and the other to specialised technology. It is divided into four phases, the first of which concentrates on their engineering practice in workshop, manufacturing and design aspects. The second gives an understanding of the whole of the installed plant and how it is run. The third is a more detailed look at one area of the work, showing in effect what I am trying to describe in this chapter, the 'daily round' of those who manufacture new plant. In the final phase the graduates take on their first appointment with what is called 'directed objective training', which is what I would describe as working with someone still holding your hand, for it is a big step to have responsibility of this kind thrust on you if you stand entirely alone.

During training, salaries in 1983 were £6685 for the first

year, £6938 for the second year, and after training, salaried posts are graded on merit. (You can begin running when you like and leave off when you like.) The only entry ticket is a 2nd class Honours degree. Acceptance is done by attending an assessment centre during the Easter vacation of your final year at university.

THE SMALLER FIRMS

It would be quite wrong to infer from the above example that the best careers in engineering lie with the big organisations. It is not given to everyone to settle for being a 'little fish in a big pool'. The personality of many of us is such as to want to be a 'big fish in a little pool' and certainly few of us will ever make it to the grade of 'big fish in big pool', nor would ever want to.

So let me put the whole of the engineering industry into some kind of perspective for you by saying that in 1981/82 there were only twenty-four organisations in Britain, involved in engineering, who each employed more than 5000 people. (And if the CEGB is typical of these, then as we have seen, about one quarter of these are professional engineers.) 379 firms employed between 1000 and 5000 people; 518 employed between 500 and 1000; 915 employed between 250 and 500; 2276 employed between 100 and 250; 7489 had only between 25 and 100 employees whilst 13,001 registered companies employed between 1 and 25 people only.

You can make up your own graphs from these and similar figures. For example, if you take the number of people in the whole country working for the various sizes of engineering firm, the results are shown in Table 8.1.

The only thing to bear in mind, however, is that the proportion of professional engineers employed by the big firms is considerably higher than that of the smaller firms, shrinking to perhaps 1 or 0 for the 1–25 employee group.

The Engineering Industry Training Board, who supplied the above figures, also provide an alternative form of classification in which the numbers in the various skills are

Table 8.1

No. of employees per firm	No. of firms	Total employees
Over 5000	24	218,000
1000–5000	379	714,000
500–1000	518	353,000
250–500	915	323,000
100–250	2276	352,000
25–100	7489	357,000
1–25	13,001	144,000

separated out, although this is not as helpful as it might be for it distinguishes between 'managerial', 'supervisory', 'administration and business' and 'professional engineers' from which one could assume, either that some employees in the first three categories are also professionally qualified, or that some of the 'professional engineers' are engaged in the first three occupations! They also appear to lump together 'technician' and 'technician engineers'. Nevertheless the figures are interesting, especially as they separate the men from the women (see Table 8.2). It is still very much a man's world, but it will change!

WOMEN IN ENGINEERING

The scarcity of women reading engineering at university is not a sharp step from equal numbers of school-leavers who have science 'A' levels to a select small percentage of women who have resisted the 'engineering is a grubby-looking man with a spanner' image and taken a chance on it. The thinning out begins much further back. The school attitude generally still persists that science is a boys' subject and in 1981, of the total number of pupils taking physics at 'O' level, only 25·5% were girls. At 'A' level the figure was only 19.5%. When you consider that physics is a basic subject for medicine, dentistry,

Table 8.2

Type of employee	Thousands of men	Thousands of women
Operator	604	227
Craft	469	1.9
Technician	200	4.8
Professional engineer	71	2.2
Clerical and office	75	198
Administration and business	127	20
Supervisory	117	9.1
Managerial	130	4.3
Unskilled	167	35

astronomy and a number of other occupations including particle physics, space research and, of course, the teaching of physics itself, a quarter of the 19·5% using it as the start of an engineering career is perhaps a reasonable proportion by which girls accept that engineering is just for boys. It means that of every five with 'A' level physics who are going on to read engineering only one is a girl, but this is 20% and a lot better than the 4–5% one is inclined to read into the final university figures.

But by rejecting what science and technology has to offer, girls are closing the door on a whole range of careers. An Engineering Council leaflet on the subject remarks:

This is particularly true at the present time when the introduction of new technology into many sectors of industry is increasing the demand for a technologically skilled workforce.

From all the information available it is clear that in the present economic climate, the sciences, engineering and technology offer better prospects for employment than many areas which have previously attracted girls and women.

The result of such thinking was that in 1984 the Equal Opportunities Commission and the Engineering Council launched an operation with the code letters WISE '84

(Women into Science and Engineering) to put special emphasis on drawing the attention of potential women engineers on the one hand, and the educationalists and industrialists on the other, to an environment which is attractive and supportive of girls and women and which is recognised as such.

The result is a very extensive programme of activities throughout the year, spread geographically over the whole of the UK, from Plymouth and Brighton to Glasgow and Dundee. Four primary schools and eleven secondary schools are acting as activity centres for a range of projects including lectures, displays of work, visits to engineering and computer companies, conferences and engineering open days.

Local education authorities are organising such activities as 'WISE weeks' where many schools within the area will concentrate on the topic at the same time, local industry co-operating. No fewer than sixty-one universities, colleges and polytechnics are offering something special for women in engineering this year. For example, the South East London College is running a basic electronics course primarily for women with no qualifications relevant to the subject. Lucy Cavendish College, Cambridge, offers the opportunity for women over the age of 25 to take a first degree in engineering. Brighton Polytechnic is running a 2½-day residential course for sixth-form girls on 'Civil Engineering for Girls', and so on.

Other organisations involved range from the professional institutions to commercial organisations such as British Aerospace, Granada TV and GEC, and on to bodies such as the Design Council, the British Association for the Advancement of Science and the Royal Society of Arts.

WISE '84 ought to make a noticeable impact on the number of girls choosing engineering as a profession; we shall just have to wait and see, but quite apart from anything else, as Viscount Caldecote said in opening the first conference of the WISE '84 year: 'We need all the help we can get and women must play their part at every level.'

We shall not get it if schools continue some of their awful practices of the past, a few of which regrettably remain. One is quoted in the same conference as that just mentioned, by

Dr E. H. Smith of Preston Polytechnic: 'My daughter was in
a class when the space shuttle was launched and a teacher
burst in and said, "Any boys want to watch the space shuttle
being launched?"'

I would recommend any young lady who has read this far
to write for a copy of the Report of the National Conference
of the Standing Conference on Schools' Science and Technology held at the Institution of Civil Engineers on 17
November 1983 (Address: The Secretary, SCSST, 1 Birdcage
Walk, London SW1H 9JJ) and read all of it. Then give it to a
friend.

REWARDS AND FRUSTRATIONS

Financial gain, job opportunities and security of career I have
already mentioned briefly under the heading 'The full life',
but there are more personal rewards which for many are at
least as important as any of these and affect personal happiness
in at least as large a measure. Viscount Caldecote exposed one
of them in his address at the WISE '84 Conference to which
I have just referred in the previous section.

Secondly, we need to get over the excitement, the challenge and the
satisfaction of engineering and science. . . . To work on a ship for a
year or two, and then see it launched and fitted out, and then sail
away to the seven seas—that is satisfaction. It is the same, if you have
been involved, to see the first flight of an aircraft, the first run of an
engine, or even a small piece of test equipment that you have
designed and made yourself.

To this I would only add—'especially the last item'! From
the day you first get exhilaration (almost surprise!) from the
fact that something *you* thought of actually works, and is
useful; you will gain in confidence at every new venture and
begin to take on bigger and bigger challenges. Behind it all
will grow a feeling that you are contributing in a real sense to
improving the quality of life for people all over the world. I
would also go so far as to say that if your project fails, it does
not mean that your efforts themselves have been a failure.

You will have more experience at the end of it, and some of the techniques and ideas you put into it will come in useful another time.

Obviously it isn't *all* good! What are the frustrations? For me the greatest is the *waiting*. It starts with waiting for 'O' level results and ends with waiting for essential equipment to be delivered. One could say that impatience is a child's prerogative. 'You can have a cake when we get home' or 'You can have it for your birthday' and similar parental phrases are often followed by 'But I wannit *NOW!*' This in-built immediacy, which is probably part of the animal in us, suppressed as it is in an adult, nags away when an exciting project needs a part for which there is a 'thirteen-week delivery'. This phrase, an '*x*-week delivery' was coined some time after World War II and in many cases is little more than an excuse for laziness on somebody's part, somewhere in the system. Backlogs tend to be cumulative, to grow like fungi so that of the thirteen weeks it takes to deliver the part, eleven are taken up by the original order spending its time in a pigeonhole. The 'paperwork' has become the nightmare of many a good project and lost many an overseas order.

What is perhaps the worst feature of this is that the paper-work, the waiting time and the frustration tend to increase with the size of organisation involved. In the following story the organisation is a nation, a nation at war, where you might think that urgency was the keynote. But everyone will agree that in massive exercises such as this one *must* have an *organisation*, or all is lost.

I make no apology for recalling the following incident, even though it is forty years old and a World War II story proper. One hopes that nothing so horrific occurs nowadays, but one never knows! I tell the story because for me, it is the ultimate in frustration for an engineer.

My civilian 'boss' at the Royal Aircraft Establishment at Farnborough in 1943 wanted some plywood. It was *vital* in the development of his project. It just *had* to be plywood. (Practically the whole aeroplane was made of it!) He went to main stores, which was run by a man so familiar with the frustrations of war that his answer, 'We haven't got any', had become a habit rather than a considered reply. But at the statement, 'I want some plywood,' he burst into laughter: 'Plywood?—PLYWOOD!—I haven't seen any plywood in years.' My boss asked him politely if he would care to rotate his body through 180° about the vertical (he was a physicist, my boss!) and tell him what THAT was leaning against the wall. 'That?—oh yeah, that's plywood' (then hastily) 'but that's for Squadron Leader Johnson—ordered it six months ago at least. You can't have any of that.' (It was a whole sheet 8′ × 6′. My boss needed 2 square feet only.) 'Would that be Squadron Leader Johnson in C-flight?' 'Yes, why?' 'Never mind.'

My boss went to see the Squadron Leader, whose reaction to being told that his valuable commodity lay in store was, 'Plywood?'—for ME?—are you SURE?—Oh yes, I *do* remember having ordered some plywood, ages ago. I had despaired of it ever coming—used something else instead.' 'Does that mean *you* don't want it and *I* can have it?' said my boss, aglow with excitement. 'Certainly, old boy.' 'And will you sign me a piece of paper to that effect?' (the *vital* bit of paper). 'Of course.'

Back to main stores went my hero with his chit. 'I want 2 square feet of that plywood. Here's my authority.' The storekeeper's eyes narrowed to slits as he read it. His head began to move slowly from side to side. 'Oh no. If that plywood is not used for the purpose for which it was originally ordered it has to go back to the main depot at Oxford.' And back to the main depot it went!

In the later years of the Tracked Hovercraft project (one of the greatest frustrations of my whole engineering career) I met a German engineer, obviously about my age, obviously very fit; I was tempted to test the Teutonic humour. At a lull in our technical discussions I ventured: 'I find it a strange world. I would guess that thirty years ago you and I were both wearing uniforms and had each taken an oath to kill each other.' He shrugged his shoulders: 'I suppose so.' 'Well,' I said, remembering the plywood incident, 'I don't know what the organisation on your side was like but ours was b——y awful, and we won!' He didn't even raise a smile.

Instead he said quite quietly, 'You are absolutely right. Our organisation was terrible—especially near the end.'

So it is roughly the same the world over, but I sincerely hope that the frustrations in waiting in *your* engineering careers never get any bigger than 'mini plywood incidents'.

But here too is another aspect of the challenge of engineering. Never believe that engineering is only about 'things'. It is about organisation, about supply and demand, most of all it is about *people*. If you detect, as I often have, falling standards in delivery dates, servicing, spare part availability, and so on, then it could be up to you to help put it right.

FALLING STANDARDS

Nor are the falling standards in waiting times the only frustrations in the daily lives of engineers. One detects falling standards in quality of materials, in design and worst of all in workmanship, and without malice, a lot of the blame can be laid at the feet of the accountant and, to be fair, the accountant can usually justify it. So again, it may fall to your lot to have some power to put some of it right, but it will invariably be a fight.

You have only to repair a headlamp on a car (of reliable make) to see the evils in a self-tapping screw. Study the post-war tools for screws, nuts and bolts, the 'Allen key', the 'Posidrive' and other tools that work from the *inside* of the screw or nut as opposed to the *outside*, as do a conventional screwdriver and a spanner, and you will realise that today's tools were made for putting screws *in*, never for taking them *out*, after rust has taken its toll. Perhaps I am old-fashioned, but in my engineering world machines are for taking apart when they go wrong and not merely to be thrown away.

Frustrations in engineering are many, and range all the way from breaking a 10 BA tap in a piece of metal that you personally have worked on for many hours to get it to that stage, to being told that the project on which you and a whole team have been working for five years, and which is near to completion, has been cancelled by government.

At the risk of being criticised as being a romantic (what's wrong with an engineer being a romantic?) I am reminded of a verse from the stage musical version of *Don Quixote*:

And the world will be better for this
That one man, torn and covered with scars,
Still strove with his last ounce of courage
To reach the unreachable stars.

Are those seemingly flowery words so far from the inscription around the Lamme Medal of the IEEE which I quoted on p. 1. 'The engineer views hopefully the hitherto unattainable'?

9

The Many Faces of Engineering

'The best person to decide what research is to be done is the man doing it . . .'

(C. K. Mees, former Director of Research for Kodak)

CLASSIFICATION

It is probably true of any facet of human knowledge that each new year brings new thinking, new books, often new hardware and inventions and new theories—AND IT NEVER GETS EASIER! To describe the engineering profession in Victorian times was a relatively straightforward task. But the complexities of modern society and the new engineering knowledge *per se* that have built up in the past half-century have made it difficult even to give but a glimpse into what a career in engineering might be like. One can only perhaps compare it with the task of writing a book for an alien being in another galaxy in an attempt to describe what the living creatures on earth are like. Being human we would at once seek the shelter of classification, beginning perhaps naturally with the obvious: animals, birds, reptiles, fishes, insects, plants, and describing each group in terms of a typical species. Later on it would be necessary to elaborate and explain that whilst these are the more obvious groups, there are many others such as Arachnids (which include spiders), Nematodes (worms), Crustacea (crabs, etc.), Radiolaria (micro-organisms that live in the sea) and many others.

But then one could re-classify them according to the ways in which they reproduce: by seeds, eggs, incubation inside each other, or by their methods of locomotion: flight, swimming, crawling, running, swinging from tree branches. One could classify them by colour, size, shape, by their feeding habits. The complexity of Life is comparable with the complexity of engineering, and it is difficult to know how to begin without boring the reader on the one hand or being deliberately confusing on the other.

Perhaps a middle course might be to describe the different departments of a large firm concerned with making products that people will want to buy, such as chairs, washing machines, television sets, railway vehicles and power-station generators. At once the difficulties are apparent. The factory making chairs will be a very different-looking place from the one making power-station generators. The people working there will be very different kinds of people, and the processes of manufacture will be different.

RELATIONSHIPS BETWEEN DEPARTMENTS

Nevertheless a typical manufacturer of consumable goods is very likely to include the following departments:

- (1) Research
- (2) Design
- (3) Development
- (4) Manufacturing
- (5) Test
- (6) Production
- (7) Marketing
- (8) Sales

plus (9) Management

and (10) Education

In the minds of most people not involved directly in engineering or anything near it, the above order looks as if it is how things really happen. The research department invents new products or improvements to existing products. Then the designers get to work to see how these can be made or incorporated so as either to (a) be most reliable, (b) be safest, (c) involve minimum factory changes, or most likely (d) make most profit!

The manufacturing department say that what is proposed is difficult to make, so the development department is called in to modify the original design which perhaps took no account of the cost of alternative materials, or shapes of parts, or finishes and appearance. Finally the ideas are ready to be put to the test and prototypes are manufactured and tested. Almost inevitably there are faults discovered at this stage, so the over-used phrase 'back to the drawing board' really means going back to the development department for help. Finally, when all is well, the article goes into production, after which it is up to the sales promoters to sell it and the marketing department to find new groups of people who might be prepared to give it a try. Advertising must be well organised; it is a highly competitive facet of the business today.

Well—*sometimes* that is the way it goes, but not often. Let us take the most ridiculous case first, just to make the point. If the commodity being made is a power-station generator capable of delivering 550 million watts, whose rotor is 14 feet long and whose cost does not bear thinking about, you do not go through processes (1) to (6) as listed above and then leave your sales people to cry out, 'Who would like to buy one of these generators?'—for the answer is no one! It will not fit their national power system. It wasn't what they had planned in their next five-year budget. The customer is a nation, not an individual. With such a product the order of the list of departments given above is almost reversed.

The first thing you do is to sell it!

You do this before you have considered how you are going to make it; perhaps even whether you *can* make it. But you have to try and you have to quote a price, or someone else will beat you to it; probably someone overseas. The salesman can only be guided by the advice and experience of his colleagues in design and manufacture, and perhaps now you can see that this kind of salesman is a very different kind of person with a very different kind of education and training from the salesman (please excuse me if I avoid the awful modern practice of referring to a 'salesperson' as is done for policeperson, postperson and a lot of other professions where their one-time monopoly by men gave them the tail end 'man' or 'men'. I mean no disrespect to the 'female of the species' if I refer to draughtsman, foreman, fireman, etc. Taken to its logical conclusion I suppose one should say: 'I got a lovely Christmas present this year—a chessboard in solid ebony and ivory and a set of chesspersons to match!')— where was I?—oh, yes—from the salesman whose job it is to sell micro-switches for refrigerator doors.

So if you meet a stranger at a cocktail party and in polite conversation ask what he does and receive the answer: 'I'm an engineer', you might proceed to ask: 'And what do you do?' and receive the reply: 'I'm a salesman with GEC.' This does not tell you whether he goes to South American or African developing countries trying to sell them whole power stations, or whether he goes around small manufacturing firms trying to persuade them to use a new kind of self-insulating screw. He might even just sit in the same office every day receiving orders and examining them to see what demands they make on delivery date, price reductions for quantity, and so on, and then negotiating with his own colleagues in the factory to see if anything can be done to meet the prospective customer at least half-way. Or he may be in advertising, which would still make him a salesman.

THE MANUFACTURE OF A LARGE OBJECT

But to return to the 'batting order' for the power station generator. Assume your sales team sells one to Brazil. The design department goes to work to see how it can be made. They come across snags and get the development department to help out. Finally a design is agreed. There is no prototype in this case; you cannot afford it at the size, although specific parts which are new might be made and tested. Scale modelling is usually too hazardous to be reliable. There comes a day when you have to take your courage (as a firm)—and this is where management comes in—and make the decision to manufacture the beast.

It goes on test and fails to meet the customer's requirements—PANIC.

Development department are asked what modifications are necessary to make it come up to specification. That department does a good job and then tells management what it will cost. The overall cost is found to be greater than that quoted as selling price to the customer—GREATER PANIC!

It is at this late stage in the process, with 95% of the machine already on the shop floor and the money spent, that research department (number (1) on the original list) are called in to try to redeem the mess your salesmen got you into by 'blowing their mouths off' to make sure a Swedish firm didn't get the order. (Meanwhile of course, the engineers of the Swedish firm have had *their* research department working round the clock in shifts to discover how the h— that British firm can possibly do it at the price!) Note that if your saleman had indeed lost the order, the situation *vis-à-vis* the research departments would merely have been reversed.

'I'm in research' used to be a boast made at cocktail parties by those with higher degrees who considered themselves the '*crème de la crème*'. No longer—only in the cloistered ivory towers of universities are there people who sit in isolation doing pure research into engineering techniques that will revolutionise the world. This might have been true except that the vast majority of engineering professors spend a lot of their time in the 1980s working hand-in-glove with industry on research contracts, which are often cheaper for the industrial firm than keeping a large research department of their own.

MARKETING

One thing is clear from the above example of the power-station generator, and that is that a very large number of engineers spend a large part of their time talking to other engineers, and very little time doing experiments or making things. Not one in a hundred of them is likely to have held a spanner from start to finish of the project—unless his car broke down on the way to work.

When the articles manufactured (commonly known as the 'end product') are small the structures of the marketing and sales departments are quite different from those of the firm making turbo-generators. Marketing will have a strong section labelled 'market research', which tries to find out what other similar firms are doing about improving their radio sets, or whatever, and some of this work comes as near to industrial espionage as makes no difference! The other half tries to estimate the demand for a new product, and this may well be done by people not at all qualified in engineering, but good at talking to people. So 'sales' again comes first in the list but if each article made costs very little indeed, you can dispense with prototypes and try to flood the market with your product before your competitor does. Here you need the production engineer to help you make sure you are not left stranded if the sales exceed your wildest dreams. You need the production engineer for other purposes as well, of course: to streamline your manufacturing methods and cut costs, to keep an eye on how 'the opposition' make virtually the same commodity, and so on, and this type of engineer was not really included in any of the departments (1) to (10) in the original list.

For relaxation, engineers play squash, badminton—football or cricket on Saturdays, and other competitive games. But the competition is never so fierce as it is in the job itself. And the prizes in the latter are very, very much bigger!

DAILY LIFE

It is easy to assume from reading an account of a big engineering project, such as building a dam, a bridge or a 20,000 h.p. rolling mill motor that most of the engineers' time, whatever their department within the organisation, is used in travelling to see people, eating big lunches, talking tactics, talking money (above all things) and reaching decisions that have little to do with anything but *experience*. What happened to all that physics we learned for 'A' level and all the lectures on engineering science we had at university? Do engineers ever actually *use* any of it, apart from teaching it to others if they happen to choose an academic career?

The short answer is that they do; many almost all the time. But the complexities of the average manufactured article make it essential that they use some kind of 'shorthand' in order to converse with others, and this often consists of breaking down the whole structure into sub-structures and then into sub-sub-structures and finally into components, each of which tends to have letters or numbers to identify it. So a technical conversation tends to sound like: 'What did you do about the low volts on the ASC?' 'I tried a new P11 in the RCI but that didn't seem to do the trick so I concluded that it must be the FW that had the fault on and not the ASC.'

These letters are not a disguise to prevent industrial espionage if the conversation happens to be taking place in the local pub. They are the result of familiarity with a mechanism whereby they get tired of keep saying 'automatic search counter' and 'follow-up unit'. So they become ASC and FUU, which latter of course is FW!

'KNOW-HOW'

But when you consider the background scientific knowledge needed to lead the second engineer in this conversation to deduce that a particular sub-unit (perhaps a temperature-controlled switch) called a 'P11' in the RCI would cure a fault in the ASC you realise just how much expertise the engineer has. What is more, a lot of it can be labelled 'accumulated know-how', which is not so much 'A' level physics as a new kind of rule book that says every time you see *this* particular kind of fault in *that* particular piece of equipment, you put a fresh capacitor in the third rack on the left.

When you think of it, this is no less a scientific piece of learning than remembering that the force on a conductor of length l situated in a field of strength B and carrying a current i will experience a force Bli at right angles to both B and i

according to a (literally) 'rule of thumb' (Fleming's left hand rule). Of course you could go to relativistic mathematics and *prove* the formula $F = Bli$, but even the physicist has his short cuts. All I am saying is that the engineer has many, many more. It does not mean that he has forgotten the background stepping stones of fundamental physics and mathematics that led up to the know-how because one day, when he is really 'up against it' he may need to go back to 'square one'.

What is interesting these days is that 'know-how' has come to be recognised as a saleable commodity, and it is not uncommon to be worth more in cash than is the licence to use a patent. The patent gives you the bare bones. You need the skilled engineer, who is often the inventor on the patent himself, to supply the know-how.

ANALOGY AND DUALITY

Once a well-tried and tested set of analogies has been in use, there will often emerge a recognisable pattern that brings with it a confidence that even if the analogues are not true, they will make a discipline that will be hard to fault, because Nature appears to work in patterns.

If an experienced engineer were asked to write a physics book it is most unlikely that it would be divided into sections such as heat, light, sound, magnetism and electricity. It is much more likely to be divided into topics such as symmetry, scaling, duality, series/parallel, phase and so on. Scaling especially is an art in itself, whilst the subject of series and parallel goes a lot further than the two familiar formulae $R = R_1 + R_2$ and $1/R = 1/R_1 + 1/R_2$. Ask yourself, for example, why in the British electricity grid system that supplies all our homes and factories with electric power, all the supplies are in *parallel*. At first sight the alternative of all houses being in series seems horrific—one break and the whole country is plunged into darkness! This, however, is no different from the present parallel system where the same voice might cry out: 'One spanner dropped across the terminals short circuits the whole system.' Darkness again! But we protect against the short circuits by fuses and circuit breakers that immediately isolate and disconnect the offending piece of equipment containing the spanner. You can do just the same for the series system and the open circuit, in fact you can list the comparable phenomena and pieces of equipment under the two systems side-by-side, as shown in Table 9.1, and so on.

Table 9.1

	Parallel	*Series*
The 'enemy'	A short circuit	An open circuit
The protector	A fuse (makes an open circuit)	A contactor (makes a short circuit)
Detection of a fault	By excess current	By excess voltage
Power rates of a piece of equipment	By amount of current taken (all at same voltage)	By amount of voltage needed (all at same current)
Allowance for large/small consumer	By voltage transformer	By current transformer

It is during such a comparison that one becomes aware of the idea of 'duals' and 'duality'. Voltage is to current as parallel is to series, as open circuit is to short circuit. Both systems are equally possible, but the reason for choosing the parallel system was, as usual, dictated by *economics*. It was the *cheaper* system.

THE AGE OF THE ACCOUNTANT

An engineer can be likened to an explorer; indeed I found Rudyard Kipling's poem *The Explorer* written in 1898 to be remarkably full of engineering analogies, not only of that time, but of the century which was to come. And yet engineering is much more than exploration, even though the exploratory phase is a necessary first step. Whether you are proposing to make something entirely new, or merely improving an existing product, the first question to be answered is, of course:

'Can it be done at all?'

But if the answer is 'Yes' it does not give you *carte blanche* to go ahead and do it. The next question is:

'Will it be efficient?'

followed by:

'How much will it cost?'
'What profit will it make?'
'Can we do it faster than our competitors?'
'Will it sell?'

and therefore finally:

'Is it worth doing?'

Now most of these secondary questions were effectively asked by the company accountant or financial adviser, although of course the final question has to be answered by management, advised and guided by engineer, salesman and accountant alike.

I may be in the minority here, but I have long found myself regarding the accountant as my adversary (as an engineer) in that accountants are the people who try to prevent me from doing *anything*! But perhaps not, for at a recent design conference in Birmingham an engineer, speaking to an audience composed entirely of engineers, said: 'If all the accountants in Britain were placed end-to-end on Brighton beach it would be a damned good idea!' and received a tremendous ovation. Most of we engineers have felt the heavy hand of the accountant at one time or another but some of us have been aware that policy varies from nation to nation. One gets the impression that in the USA, a team of rocket experts can send an unmanned probe to a distant planet, misguidedly put spin on it to keep it straight, with the result that it leaves the atmosphere tumbling end-over-end, is detonated and written off as 'mission abort', without a single head rolling. The attitude seems to be, 'OK, we did it wrong

—so we'll do it right next time—what's $200 million anyway?' In Britain, engineers have got to get it right FIRST TIME, whether the project be large or small. They are accountable always to the money men. We must never lose sight of the fact that they are as fallible as are we.

DEALING WITH PEOPLE

I hope it is emerging, from the foregoing discussion on departments, that engineers are not the people who actually make things with their hands. They often read meters, press buttons, study computer print-outs and do other physical things, even though mostly they *talk* to other people. But they rarely operate a lathe, a milling machine, an earth-shifting machine or a crane. There is a whole army of people, these days described collectively as 'technician engineers', which is probably as fair a description as can be found. These are the men and women who implement the decisions made by management as to what shall be made and how it shall be done. Engineers advise management, and when the decisions are made, engineers instruct the technician engineers as to what they are to do.

The qualifications of a technician engineer are of course different from those of an engineer. They do not generally have degrees or equivalent qualifications. They may belong to a union, which a chartered engineer would not. Their role in the engineering output of a nation is vital. A more complete discussion on the relative qualifications, professional institutions and the like, was included in Chapter 7. I mention the topic here because being responsible for relationships between management and unions is also the job of some engineers, and since it is a job consisting almost entirely of dealing with *people* it is perhaps the most complex job of all within the profession.

Running the professional institutions is a sizeable task and employs thousands of people, many of whom are of course qualified engineers. Engineering institutions have a main function of publishing, so there are editorial staff, who must clearly understand what the material they handle is about, if only to arbitrate between authors and referees, who are constantly at each others' throats!

DIVERSIFICATION AND OVERLAP

As knowledge increases it is a natural consequence that people in a particular discipline will see their subject dividing almost like an amoeba. In the last century, young men (mostly) did a first degree in 'engineering', which included courses now exclusively confined to civil or to mechanical or to electrical engineering. In 1910 an engineer was expected to design a turbo–generator and then design the turbine to drive it.

Soon it was time to divide the discipline and for a time a triumvirate reigned consisting of, in this order of seniority:

civil, mechanical, electrical

It is quite surprising how, despite the universal application of electrical engineering (all matter is made of electrons!), the civil engineers retain their status. One is reminded forcibly of a comparable hierarchy in the armed services where the navy is the 'senior service', even though it is only too well established that aircraft and now space missiles delivering atomic weapons are currently the war-winners. There seems to be no other logic behind seniority in these organisations other than the 'We were here first' primitive territorial claim not unlike that of jungle animals!

Be that as it may, there are still universities in the UK where a newly appointed civil engineering professor, aged thirty, has final say in how the money is allocated among the engineering departments, even though the professor of mechanical engineering may have been a member of the senate for twenty years!

Soon after the 'Big Three' had set up court a fourth major engineering discipline appeared over the horizon. Aeronautical engineering was destined to overtake municipal engineering, structural engineering, and others among the older disciplines. Then production engineering was created as a discipline in its own right. Meanwhile the 'Big Three' were rapidly growing out of their clothes. Electrical engineering was sub-dividing naturally into 'heavy' and 'light', largely as the result of the birth of the triode valve—an object almost little more than a museum piece nowadays.

It is strange that within a century of engineering one sees a microcosm of evolution taking place. People born about 1910 saw the rise and fall of the cinema within their lifetime, whereas the rise and fall of the Dinosaurs is thought to have taken 150 million years. In the same way the triode valve that fathered the tetrode and the long-beloved pentode all had to go before the mightly onslaught of solid state electronics, the transistor, the thyristor, the power transistor. The process took less than a quarter of a century.

'Heavy' electrical engineers studied electrical machines and power systems, like Williamanmary who, we are told in *1066 and All That*, 'was a good King'! But soon there were separate departments for 'machines men' as opposed to 'power systems men' and machines men were sub-divided into 'synchronous machines men' and 'induction motor men'. Likewise 'light' electrical engineers divided into communications, control and automation, computing, electronics proper, microprocessors and many others, and the evolutionary growth process continued unabated with automation (at least a part of it) becoming 'robotics'. Computing split into 'hardware' and 'software' (basically engineering proper and computer programming theory and practice).

Every sub-division brought dangers. Mostly people stopped talking to people in other groups, so there was immediate danger of duplication of effort. Worse than that, one man had a problem he could not solve, and worked at it for six months unaware that immediately above him there was an engineer in another room, who was classed in another discipline, who had had the solution for over a year. The two engineers, both electricals perhaps, were only separated by a concrete floor! Publication explosion was the next danger. It has been estimated that if you write a paper for a learned society journal, and are fortunate enough to have it published, it will be read, cover to cover, by 1·8 people in the whole of time (on average). If it is a mathematical paper it will be read by 0·1 of a person in the same time!

We need a better communication system and there are engineers working on that too. Data extraction and circulation is a major problem. So too can be language, which is where the mathematician has last laugh since his language is almost universal and shorthand to boot! (Sin θ is written 'sin θ' even in Russian.)

But there are also compensations. Within such an autonomous system of diversification, quite unlike the natural bifurcations of a river forming a delta, there are bound to be overlaps; and the overlaps are not confined to the engineering profession. What shall you call a man who did his first degree in physics, but spent the whole of his final year attending lectures in electronics in the electrical engineering department of the same university, then went into industry and became involved in the manufacture of cathode-ray tubes for TV sets, thought of some new ideas, patented them and later became Professor of Electron Optics in a university engineering department?—obviously it ceased to matter a long time ago. Was Michael Faraday a physicist, a chemist or an engineer? For me he was wholly engineer—is he not my patron saint?—but for someone else he will be whatever they want him to be. What I think we might all agree is that he remains the greatest experimenter of all time, in any subject. What an older engineer like myself tends to regret is that a smaller proportion of engineers is now engaged in experimental work than ever before, whilst in universities there are more and more demands for management training, although there can be no doubt that those whose preference is for administering the subject will get as much job satisfaction as those who still prefer to go out seeking new territories—and will probably be better paid.

NEW FACETS

One message that must never be forgotten, however, is that no matter what anyone tells you to the contrary about any one aspect of the subject—it *hasn't* 'all been done'! I was told this about thirty-five years ago in respect of induction motors, but what followed was to show precisely the opposite. I believe this to be true of most subjects. When there appears to have been stagnation or saturation of one particular line of study subsequent history has shown that we have barely scratched the surface. I have often found that the most successful engineers, in any facet of its many sub-divisions, are those who become totally committed to a project or idea until they eat, drink and sleep the subject and bore their colleagues to death by reverting to it every time there is a lull in a casual conversation, even though the latter may have been about the quality of the food, or the beer, or last night's television play, or the opposite sex—this order of priority is deliberately stolen from *Omar Khayyám*:

> Here with a Loaf of Bread beneath the Bough,
> A Flask of Wine, a Book of Verse—and Thou

Engineering was traditionally a 'man's world' and cannot yet claim to have really emerged from it. True, women in engineering are now increasing in numbers, but until we increase the proportion of women undergraduates in university engineering courses from the 4 or 5%, which it is at present in several of the oldest and well-established universities, they will not really have taken their place alongside the men and provided that new face of engineering that will be as welcome as that of the bride coming to the altar.

GOOD AND BAD ENGINEERING

In a world where imperfections are often to be exploited as well as spurned, where nothing is perfect and everything is a compromise, and where, in a real sense, there is no truth, it is often difficult to know what is 'good' and what is 'bad' in engineering, within the traditional meanings of those words. I have already referred to 'fashion' (p. 15) and the answer in part lies here. It also lies in what might be called 'morals', and surely if one is writing about morals, the subject of fashion is bound to be involved. One has only to look at what was taboo on television in the late 1950s and what passes as acceptable for children to see and hear in the 1980s, to see how attitudes to morals change in fashion almost as rapidly as attitudes to women's clothes, although in the case of morals the 'skirts' only appear to get continually shorter whereas the dictates of the Paris fashion houses cause them to oscillate up and down with almost sine-wave-like periodicity!

The question of 'good' engineering must involve the question, good for whom? The answers to this question can include 'the manufacturer', 'the shareholders', 'the workers', 'the nation', 'the customer' and 'the craftsman'. The variety of opinions as to what is good, given by these various groups, runs all the way from black to white. There is no doubt that the best possible materials and craftsmanship do not go into the manufacture of modern furniture, or cars, or children's toys. On the other hand, the quality of garden tools, surgeons' implements, in fact tools in general, seems to improve annually. Often one sees the anomaly of better tools to make inferior products!

But for a really good example of where undeniably immoral practices receive the commendation of management, one can go right back to the 1930s where a well-known multiple store included a pet department and the pet department sold goldfish in glass bowls. The department was located on the ground floor with only escalators taking people *up*—having made your purchases on the higher floors you could damned well *walk* down! This facet alone should have told you something about how this particular firm cared more for its profits than for its customers! In the store was a suggestions box, and one day an employee put in a slip of paper suggesting that if the goldfish were sold on the *top* floor, the jostling on the stairs on the way out would cause many a bowl to be broken and only a callous brute would leave a struggling goldfish to die on the steps—probably trodden underfoot by someone else who would also suffer mentally from the experience. Besides, the recipient of the

151

fish would generally be a child who would scream the place down if the fishy were not rescued. The dash up to the top floor for another bowl was virtually 100% certain. By increasing the risk of breakage, the profits from the pet department would undoubtedly rise, especially if the move was accompanied by a rise in the price of bowls. Of course the idea was implemented and the employee who suggested it received a bonus in his pay packet for the rest of his career in the store. Anything more blatantly immoral would be difficult to find—but good salesmanship, good business?—undoubtedly. One felt a burning desire to stick a notice in that pet department—'We sell goldfish in broken bowls.'

Toys in general have always been a target for the unscrupulous manufacturer who designs them with a deliberately built-in weak link designed to fail sometimes within the hour. But what about ourselves? Were we not designed to fail after 'three score years and ten'? And was it not good bio-engineering that it should be so? (More support for the 'God is an engineer' theorem, but one so close to the bone, so far as upsetting the bishops is concerned, that I had better leave this debate to individual readers.) Certainly it used to be a lot less than seventy years, and we have been fighting to increase it for centuries and are clearly succeeding.

But in engineering, progress has been even more rapid and seems to have brought with it a tendency to shorten the 'lives' of manufactured articles. No one wants a dishwasher or vacuum cleaner or lawnmower that will last twenty years. 'In five years time there will be a "super de luxe" model that my next door neighbour will have, and *I* shall want one', is a natural human reaction. In the new fashions in engineering, such as video games, it is difficult to keep track of just *what* the latest developments are, so rapid is the progress. The word 'obsolete', almost unknown at the beginning of the century, features more and more frequently in engineering discussions, whether between salesmen or designers or manufacturers.

And so far as morals are concerned it is but a short step from the clearly immoral breakable toy to the 'built-in-obsolescence' concept that the Americans brought with them to Europe in the war years of 1940. In the majority of cases, genuine built-in obsolescence can in no way be branded as immoral, even though it may offend the craftsman who would still declare it 'bad engineering'. On purely economic grounds built-in obsolescence is clearly 'good engineering'. Ideally, all parts of a mechanism should wear out at the same time, but if this is found not to be the case, then make the longer-lasting parts of something cheaper and inferior that *will* wear out when the weakest part wears out.

But biology, as usual, provides a glorious enigma on the subject of good and bad. The common woodlouse has remained unchanged for 600 million years. It survived the ice ages, the rise and fall of the mighty dinosaurs, even the coming of the potential enemy of all living creatures —man! What was once said of the capabilities of an individual man is surely as true of the ability of the humble woodlouse:

'To withstand in the evil day, and having done all, to stand.'

—And yet—it poses the question: is the woodlouse an example of a good design or a bad one? 'Good!' is the immediate first reaction of most people. 'Bad!' says the experienced engineer after some thought. 'Its design is so inflexible that it never progressed.'

This of course at once opens the bar parlour debate on whether it is our purpose on Earth *to* progress, but after invoking evolution in general and Divine Guidance in particular, it would appear as if it were some kind of duty of each generation to improve on the last in thought, in ethics, in ingenuity, in sheer knowledge and certainly in wisdom. If it were not true of engineering too, there would be no fundamental research of any kind being conducted, so with apologies to the rugged and durable woodlouse— it is a bad piece of engineering on Nature's part, one might even put it down by labelling it 'one of Nature's many cul-de-sacs!'

THE EXPLOITATION OF IMPERFECTIONS

One attitude of an engineer that has much in common with the ways of Nature is that adopted towards imperfections. School physics tends to regard high efficiency as the 'be-all and end-all' in such things as machines, friction as a nuisance because it produces heat loss, and zero resistance in an electric circuit as 'Utopia'.

Now an engineer will generally sacrifice from a small percentage to a more considerable loss of efficiency if, by doing so, substantial improvements can be gained in such commodities as power/weight ratio, power/cost ratio, power factor (in the case of electrical machines), transportability and so on. Let it be said, despite earlier derogatory remarks about the accountant, that it was the latter profession that taught the engineer about 'overall economics'.

Friction is a quite different matter. Without friction all nuts threaded on to bolts that are open-ended at the bottom would *always* fall off, so a car would literally collapse into a heap of parts within seconds of friction ceasing to be effective. No ladders could rest against walls, no knots could be tied in ropes or string, and worst of all, we should not be able to propel ourselves along smooth ground, whether by car, train, bicycle or on foot! On the slightest slope, we should always end up at the bottom. One *could* exist, but it would be a strange world indeed devoid of all friction.

The legend of the foolish King Midas who asked the gods to make all objects that he touched turn to gold is well known. A very similar phenomenon almost happened in respect of superconductivity. When a metal is cooled to a temperature lower than 3°K its resistivity appears to drop dramatically down to zero. 'Geronimo!' was the cry. 'What a great substance for wiring up circuits.' But the engineering gods were more merciful to the engineers than were Midas' gods. They left just a tiny bit of resistance there. Why was that important?

When electric current flows it always produces magnetic field and thereby a circuit has a property we call 'inductance'

(*L*). Now when a current is first switched on it does not reach its full value at once but rises exponentially to that value with a time constant of L/R where R is the resistance of the circuit. At very low temperatures the inductance is unaffected, but if R shrinks to zero—literally ZERO—the time constant becomes infinite and you can never get a current to start! When it was proposed to link the City of Birmingham into the national electricity grid by means of a superconducting cable (including the small amount of resistance left in it by the merciful gods) it was estimated that it might take over four hours after closing the switch before the full power was flowing!

Magnetic field that 'leaks' from all practical magnetic circuits produces a 'leakage inductance' often regarded as a nuisance because it causes voltage drops from generators when delivering load, it lowers power factor, also efficiency to a lesser extent, and the stray field may interfere with neighbouring telephone lines and other apparatus. But that same leakage flux is used to devastating effect by the designers of direct-on-line starting induction motors to limit starting current and shape the speed/torque characteristic, and by designers of power systems to limit short circuit current during a fault until the circuit breakers have had time to operate.

The engineer is ever mindful of the opportunity to *exploit* imperfections, as well as the need in other situations to limit them to a minimum.

Nature, of course, is full of imperfections, the most noticeable of all perhaps being the fact that not all offspring in the litter of a mammal are equally strong, so the 'survival of the fittest' law ensures an increasingly strong race of creatures. As a tree dies and the main trunk breaks off in high wind, the stump becomes a home for beetles, woodlice and hundreds of other creatures, none of which were strong enough to penetrate the perfect living tree.

Quite the strangest exploitation of imperfections I have ever seen in Nature was brought to my notice by the Plant Protection Division laboratories of ICI near Maidenhead in Berkshire. There the chemists who experiment with weed-killers would ideally like 100 'standard weeds', all of the same size, growing at the same rate, on which to test perhaps 50 experimental weedkillers. So about 2000 seeds of the selected weed are sown and from the seedlings, 500 are pricked out into boxes for rapid rearing. But within a fortnight some have raced away and are obviously soon to become 'giant' weeds. Others have noticeably begun to shrink! After about six weeks you have the 500 divided roughly into three groups: giants, normals and runts. Never mind, we will plant out the 170 normals into separate pots. They will be enough for our initial experiments. After a fortnight in the pots, the same phenomenon begins. Some actually shrink! Within six weeks you really have got giants, normals and runts. But you only got 50-odd normals out of the 2000 seeds with which you began.

What is the purpose of this behaviour? It is a defence mechanism. If these weeds coexisted in a lawn or field and there was a drought, the shallow-rooted runts would die within the week. The normals too would die if the drought continued, but to support the massive foliage of the giants they need deep, penetrating roots and although all of a plant above ground may die off during prolonged drought, the root lives on and, comes the first shower of rain, it begins to grow again rapidly above ground and within days will produce flowers, then seeds, which if sown produce equal quantities of giants, normals and runts!

So what purpose the runts? When a lawn is sprayed or dusted with a weedkiller the idea is that the poison adheres to the broad leaves of the daisy, dandelion, plantain, etc., but is easily washed off the thin leaves of the grass by the rain. The poison is carried to the heart of the weed and kills it. This is true in the case of the giants and normals, but not the runts, who deal with it in much the same way as the grass. The gardener is pleased. He fails to see the runts. But within a few days they seed and produce, of course, equal numbers of giants, normals and runts!

Notice that in each case the *status quo* is put right in a single generation. But the whole system is rather weird. In the first place it suggests that the runts are an indication that the weeds foresaw the coming of *Homo sapiens* and his confounded weedkillers. Secondly the behaviour of the planted-out 'normals' in the individual pots suggests that the weeds 'consciously' (?) know just what game we are up to!

There was a sharp lesson for over-zealous conservationists on one of the advertising leaflets of the Plant Protection Division. In a contrived interview, a journalist, well-known for his 'knock-anything' ability, was attacking an ICI scientist over the use of insecticides and weedkillers. The last question from the journalist asked whether the company was not afraid that it was disturbing the 'balance of Nature', to which came the sharp reply: 'There's no such thing as the balance of Nature. There's nothing so unnatural as a field of wheat!'

COMPROMISE AND CONQUER

It is our common knowledge that no one ever gets everything he or she wants. But perhaps in no other profession is it so necessary to take action on this fact. Of course we would all like our electric motors to run at 100% efficiency, to cost a few pence each per thousand horsepower and to weigh only a few grams for the same output. It is our common experience of the materials we know that such motors are not possible even though, with the incredibly rapid rises in technical knowledge that we now experience, one must add 'at present'. What is less well known, and certainly not obvious, is that it is possible to design an electric motor for a given output, be it a few watts or many megawatts, with an efficiency as near to 100% as you choose to name, 99%, 99·9%, 99·99% and so on, but the more you demand, the more you have to pay in some other way, mostly in weight and in cash. For example, a ¼ h.p. motor of 'normal' design might cost £10, weigh 18 lb and have a maximum efficiency of 65%. If you asked for a motor to deliver the same output at 80% efficiency, it might cost £100 and weigh 150 lb (it would, of course, be of proportionately larger dimensions). But if you asked for 99% efficiency, you would move into the region of thousands of pounds in cash and several tons in weight, and the motor would almost certainly not fit into the space for which you had intended it.

157

The next question therefore, is what can I have if I ask for a lower efficiency, like 20%? The answer is, not a lot cheaper, nor lighter, indeed it may again be dearer and heavier, for all the extra heat loss has to be removed and this may demand the addition of a fan, extra cooling ducts and so on. The 65% efficiency machine with which we began had already, so to speak, been 'optimised' for cost and weight, and you more or less accepted the efficiency for what it was.

What is even more surprising perhaps is that when you optimise the design of a 20 megawatt rolling mill motor for size and cost the efficiency comes out at 97·5%, as it must if it is to be useful to the customer. One gets the strange feeling that electric motors were 'intended' for humans as grass was for sheep, but the comparison is bad. Sheep *adapted* to grass; man did not have to adapt to the electric motor. He only had to learn how to extract iron and copper from minerals found in the earth and the rest was, as it were, presented to him 'on a plate'! One is reminded of an episode in Star Trek!

—And there's another thing about science and engineering. There are stranger and more exciting facts in real life than were ever dreamed by the writers of science fiction (not that engineers therefore reject science fiction; most of them seem to love it!). Some of the best science fiction is as near to fact as makes no difference. Arthur C. Clarke's *Fountains of Paradise* is more than 90% true, but none the less exciting because of that.

But to return to our main theme of compromise, it extends all the way into economics, and the accountant is much involved, of course. Basically there has to be a compromise between capital cost and running cost. Without going to the extremes of the examples given above (99% efficient, etc.) you can always have a little higher efficiency (and therefore cut your running costs) at the expense of a slightly bigger machine, but the penalty clause is a steep one in terms of capital cost.

So the balance has to be made in terms of the depreciation on capital and all the intricacies of delayed payments, tax reliefs and all the other complexities that belong in the accountancy world, and the running cost in terms of the cost of fuel, which will differ depending on whether it uses electricity, gas, crude oil or refined petrol. We are forced to the conclusion that a political speech made by a Middle Eastern leader will decide whether the slots in a turbo-alternator to be designed next year will be 5·13 cm wide or 5·87 cm!

There is compromise wherever you look.

School physics teaches you that a transformer is basically a simple device, just two coils wound around an iron core and the ratio of voltages is in proportion to the ratio of the number of turns. So if you want to reduce a voltage from 220 to 110 all you have to do is to have twice as many turns on the primary as on the secondary and the right thickness of wire to carry the current you propose to pass. But 'twice as many as what?' is a question no physics book will ever attempt to answer, because the answer is far too complex and involves economics, which is not physics!

If you wish you could choose two turns and one turn and end up with a transformer twenty times bigger than it needs to be, of which 98% is iron. You could, on the other hand, choose 2 million turns and 1 million turns and end up with a transformer 500 times bigger than necessary, of which 99·9% is copper. The 'best' answer lies somewhere between. But whether it is 960 and 480 turns, or 1020 and 510 turns, is far from obvious, and when you are in the design business you will know that it is the current prices of copper and steel that fix the precise number, so a transformer designed for the same purpose in 1980 will have slightly different numbers of turns from one designed in 1985, even though the ratio of turns will always be 2:1. That, again, is compromise.

Nature, of course, is a master of compromise. Do not imagine that the so-called 'flying foxes' *enjoy* hitting the ground with such an enormous thump! They accept it as part of the price for having the ability to glide through the air as few other mammals can. A lot of Nature's compromise, whereby many and varied creatures that prey on each other manage to live together and achieve some sort of balance (albeit with uncertainty and insecurity their daily companions), is achieved by the technique known to engineers as

159

'feedback', and it can be either positive or negative, although the positive kind almost always leads to instability, and some other phenomenon such as saturation invariably has to come to the rescue.

The biologist has summed it up nicely in a well-known phrase: 'More cats, more clover.' Translated this means that cats will catch field mice. Field mice are known to eat bees and bees pollinate clover, so more cats means fewer mice, fewer mice results in more bees, and of course more bees make more clover.

It would be easy to ask despairingly: 'What is engineering if it is not a compromise?' But do not despair, for what is marriage but a compromise and, in the end, what is Life, if not a compromise? So take up the challenge with vigour and see what fascinating new compromises you can achieve that might change the whole shape of a machine overnight, by refusing to accept the practice that has been in vogue for half a century and taking a new look at the whole problem. You can do this so much more easily in engineering because of the complexity of problems. In physics the constraints are often too tight.

10

The Way Ahead

'If I have seen further it is by standing on the shoulders of giants.'

(Sir Isaac Newton)

If there is one fashionable commodity that is likely to outstrip all others in engineering manufacture as we approach the year 2000, it is *reliability*. No longer is it only the wealthy who can afford a TV set, a vacuum cleaner, a hair drier, a fridge, a transistor radio, a record player *and* a spin drier. Hundreds of thousands of homes also have a washing machine, a tumble-air drier, a deep freeze, a video recorder, an electric razor, a motor-ised lawnmower and such luxuries as an electric toothbrush, electric carving knife, electric blanket and a home computer.

Quite apart from the possibility of blocked drains, furred-up or burst pipes, house wiring faults and all the ordinary afflictions that are sent to try us, I have listed 18 appliances in the previous paragraph, each of which could go wrong when it is most inconvenient, to say nothing of the family car, or cars, with their multiplicity of components, each prone to its own special 'annoyance' fault (like failing to start on a cold morning) and one senses a growing frustration at the number of times housewives, in particular, are prevented from going shopping or have their daily routine upset by having to 'wait for men' to come round and put this or that right.

161

Partly, of course, it is the result of falling standards, of a lack of care for the individual, but it is also simply due to the increase in the number and complexity of devices that are now available to us, a simple question of probability of failure within a few weeks of operation. A 'guarantee' certificate is not enough. The financial compensation is naturally worthwhile, but it's the *waiting*. Waiting on the part of the customer is every bit as frustrating as the waiting for drawings or parts or approval for cash on the part of the engineer which I mentioned in the previous chapter, and since the customer is the most important contributor to industrial prosperity (though sometimes you would hardly believe it), the customer will demand reliability more and more, and engineering standards will have to rise. This trend, I think, will please everyone, including the accountant, for he will always adjust his prices to take account of the improved workmanship. Which of us who has a car would not be prepared to pay *double* for our petrol if we were absolutely *sure* that our car would *never* break down, nor require maintenance? You can generally reckon, in working out income tax allowances on a car, that if you double the cost of the fuel you will just about have taken account of maintenance and repairs, of which replacement of tyres is often one of the bigger items.

Reliability and good service are the top commodities of the future, whatever engineering products are being marketed.

UTOPIA

In a well-balanced society there is low unemployment; wages are just high enough to allow cause for grumbling, for we need to grumble, it appears, and a grudge against the 'Organisation' is much to be preferred to grudges against each other. We need leisure time and luxuries to go with it, and when you put all this together you have some kind of impossibility—unless—you can organise something stupid and not let anyone know you are doing it!

It has been said, for example, that in Utopia whole factories full of people manufacture television sets with the greatest care and these are crated for export, but later the crates are marked 'industrial waste' and they are taken out to sea and dumped, and only *one person*, in the limit, need know that this practice is going on!

Of course, to do this one needs a dictatorship—a benevolent dictatorship. Almost every academic will tell you that benevolent dictatorship is the ideal form of government, adding quickly 'with corrective assassination!' This looks after the situation when it become non-benevolent. But of course, various people's ideas of benevolence differ violently, which is why Utopia for all is as impossible as perpetual motion.

Nevertheless, it is possible to see when steps in the right direction are being made, and it is up to every profession to try to put its own house in order in this respect, which is why I am returning, in the final chapter, to where I began. When young people who have joined the profession have been through the academic part and the industrial part of the training, and had only a year or two in practice, they probably have better ideas as to the way ahead than have many of those engineers who have been in the business for more years than the young members' ages.

The young people should therefore strive to make their voices heard in top management, not merely in a 'suggestions box', and this sentence is in no way an incitement to riot or to do anything like it. Older engineers with real wisdom will be the first to recognise this need and act on it, and I believe that there are enough of them to make this come about. It *must*, or we shall continue to struggle on to the end of the century with the kind of frustrations we have all suffered, one way or another, in the 1960s and 1970s. The image of Big Brother in *1984* could not have been more wrong. It has to be the young people whose opinions count for most, and what a responsibility *that* is for them. But I am vastly encouraged by the fact that when there were 'sit-ins', 'lock-outs' and other forms of student unrest in the UK universities in the 1960s, often leading to violence, engineering students were seldom behind any of it. Perhaps one reason for this is that they are worked harder than others! Certainly engineering courses at most universities are very full lives for those engaged in them.

But I hope that this is received in the spirit that someone *cares* about them rather than that pressure is being put on them for some other reason. Be assured that, unlike school teaching, no university lecturer gets promoted or reprimanded as the result of the marks his students obtain in their exams, so why should *he* care?

ENTHUSIASM AND AMBITION

Generally the answer is that he cares because he is lecturing about the subject he is fanatical about. This kind of enthusiasm easily 'rubs off' on to members of an audience. I must confess that my flare for machines was generated initially by a man at Regent Street Polytechnic in London in 1943 (a man almost old enough to be my grandfather) who lectured with such excitement about induction motors that white foam would appear at the corners of his mouth. Now I know that such fervour is alas rare, but we can all try to pass on our natural enthusiasm to others, and the risk of boredom is far better than that of appearing a cold, dull person who *must* be unhappy in his work.

One tendency among humans which has to be overcome, I am sure, is that of wanting to hide in a crowd. It is the basic shyness in all of us that is to blame, but it leads to a desire to be mediocre, to be 'just ordinary', when often the potential to be better is just bursting to be let out.

Every student in engineering who is admitted to a university course is thought to be capable of getting at least a 2nd class Honours degree. Let that therefore be considered to be a minimum and, in moderation, never be afraid of professing ambition, of going to university with the intention of getting 'a First', even though I believe there is always an element of luck attached to that honour, which is why a 'Top Second' is never divorced from it in any subsequent awards or whatever is being sought. The people who end up with 3rd class Honours or Pass degrees are often those whose aim in life is to do 'the minimum amount necessary to get the marks for a Bottom Second'.

In the same way, when you *are* qualified and you have your job and your responsibilities, never settle for second best, in materials, or workmanship, or quality generally. In the 1930s a manufactured article marked 'MADE IN ENGLAND' was itself a guarantee of the highest quality of workmanship and we should try to restore that image for the UK, both in the present European organisation and in the world generally.

TECHNOLOGICAL ADVANCES

Advances in techniques, new inventions, new materials and processes will grow like mushrooms almost without any of us trying. The whole subject of engineering will continue to divide and sub-divide, as I have indicated earlier, and in doing so there will inevitably be re-grouping and merging, until the old artificial boundaries of civil, mechanical and electrical engineers become almost totally obscured. What will be the first degree of an engineer who is an expert in robotics? It could be almost anything.

It is possible to teach physics—and hopefully it will be taught—without having to resort to separate books for heat, light, sound, magnetism and electricity. It can be taught under headings such as waves, flow, analogy, symmetry, change of state, and so on. In the same way engineering can be taught under headings such as feedback, scaling, quality, quantification, each of which spans all the descriptions at once and examples can be drawn at random from the enlightened physics courses in schools. This is not Utopia. This is the way it *has* to go or we shall stagnate and other countries will leave us behind very rapidly.

So let us be enthusiastic to the extent of being *inspired*. At all levels from university onwards, the majority of a community know who is 'going places' and who is not. The same applies in pop music, in entertainment generally, so why not in engineering. Therefore make sure that you attend the lectures of 'the Inspired', whether or not you intend answering their exam papers, for you will pass that way but *once*. Then try to work in the sections of industry that are also seen to be going places. It may not always be easy, but one thing is certain. To do so, you yourselves will have to be seen to be a 'grade above the ordinary' and this does not so much mean that you are specially gifted, but rather that you are ready to work hard, to give *all* to the job, and to be flexible in thought. It is your *attitude* that will get you noticed and wanted on the best teams who are going to the top of the profession.

True, there will always be the mediocre, and they will, almost by definition, be the majority. But by raising the level at the top, you will imperceptibly raise the level of the mediocre. How else does a good school get its reputation?

It was Isaac Newton himself who said, modestly: 'If I have seen further, it is by standing on the shoulders of giants.' Newton had very few giants on whose shoulders he could stand. The ancient philosophers, Aristotle, Plato, Archimedes and so on, Leonardo da Vinci, of course, and Galileo. It is easy to see that of the three Laws of Motion now attributed to Newton (not by himself of course) the first and third were written by Leonardo and the second by Galileo. But consider how many more 'giants' are now available to us, to have their works read and thus to have their shoulders stood upon.

Max Planck and Niels Bohr, Pauli, Enrico Fermi, Heisenberg, Einstein, Mach—the list is very long for the pure scientist. Engineers can very easily become inspired by the works of Faraday, Maxwell, Osborne Reynolds, the Brunels (father and son), Bessemer, Nikola Tesla, Boucherot, Oliver Heaviside, Barnes Wallis and many others. Their biographies might be read with profit quite early in an engineering career. To see the problems they faced, and the ways in which they overcame them, makes some of our own problems appear to shrink immediately by comparison. Faraday had to insulate all his own electric wire, which made him much more conscious of the difficulties and solutions to problems of designing magnetic circuits. We take insulated wire as a birthright. How many more facets of engineering do we take for granted that otherwise might provide us with a better insight into other problems? Being aware of what has already been achieved is an important section of one's collection of that most valuable asset—*experience*.

But in experience itself there is danger. I have often seen it used to put down good ideas of younger engineers and it tends to prevail, simply because the one with the experience is the older engineer carrying the senior rank. One wonders just how many world-beating ideas have been so treated. After all, some of the biggest money-spinners have not necessarily been huge pieces of complex equipment, for example the ready-potted plant (or tree!) that made the modern garden centre what it is, the zip fastener and the ball-point pen.

Experience, I always feel, is a commodity balanced on a razor's edge between the good and the bad in engineering. On the one hand, without it you can go blundering on to the longest set of mistakes ever seen. But with a lot of it you will end up forever making the same article today that you made yesterday, by the same process, using the same materials. Happily, the 'what was good enough for my father is good enough for me' syndrome that was rife in the 1930s has nearly died out. But we must be ever aware of what the author of *Star Wars* would call the 'Dark side of the Force'—of experience, that is; for it can so easily lead to stagnation in both thought and product.

There is danger too in an invention so brilliant that it is many years ahead of its time, for it then goes on to be used until it is just as many years behind its time. The Lancashire loom with its 'flying shuttle' was a classic example of this phenomenon, as the result of which the cotton industry in Lancashire plunged into disaster in the 1930s whilst the Swiss and the Swedes took over with entirely new processes and machinery.

Be ever aware that experience, vital as it is to doing almost anything but the instinctive, can be as big a drag on progress as it might appear to be an asset.

There is a natural by-product of experience which rapidly infiltrated the older facets of engineering, as in the case of my own profession where it affected electric motor design. A customer orders a large motor of very specific design. The company concerned knows that it must offer a competitive price, not very different from that of a standard line that they sell 'off the shelf'. So there is no time to start designing it *ab initio* using Maxwell's equations and numerous conformal transformations to try to meet the design. (I often think that perhaps many sixth-formers believe that this is how design starts.) What really happens is that the job is given to the engineer with a lot of *experience* who contemplates the customer's requirements for perhaps up to half an hour before going to a filing cabinet and pulling out the design sheet for a motor that the company built for another customer seven years ago. It was not *identical*, but very similar. So certain dimensions are changed slightly, the flux density is allowed to creep up 10% in certain places, a little extra cooling facility is added and soon the new design has been *adapted* from the old one to please the customer.

Now there is nothing wrong with this technique as an isolated example. But after a 'century of electric motor design', that 'new' machine has itself become the starting point for minor additions and alterations and after generations of this one can stand back and declare: 'This is not *design*—this is *Evolution*!' It is the evolution process carried out precisely as Nature would do it, by minor adjustments in each generation in order to adapt to the changing demands of the environment.

Engineering must never degenerate into evolution. Yet at the same time we must make use of the products of Nature's evolution, as I have indicated in Chapter 6. There is no harm at all in going right to the end of the longest engineering evolutionary chain in the world. Now I know that stagnation seems unlikely in a new industry such as power electronics or robotics, but it *will* come, unless we guard against it, as history has shown us. There is no brainwashing so powerful as self-brainwashing, and if you invent a new process which is seen to be good the forces urging you to be satisfied with it are enormous. You must *immediately* put it aside into that vast pile of experience that exists only in a 'twilight', to be drawn from when needed, but never to dominate or inhibit your thinking.

It is you, the young engineers, who can best guard against the stagnation of both experience and evolution and must make tremendous quantum-like leaps forward both by *think-*

ing new and *thinking big*. On the wall of my office I have a picture from an old calendar. It shows a kitten fast asleep in a wastepaper basket. But the picture on the outside of the basket is that of the head of a magnificent Bengal tiger and the slogan below reads 'When you dream, dream big.'

Whilst I was writing this book I overheard a splendid remark on a train passing through Horsham. It came from a child who could have been no more than three years old. My ears were first alerted to the conversation by the sentence:

Child: 'And then we'll sail back to Horsham.'
Mother: 'How would we *sail* back to Horsham, idiot child?'
Child: 'We'll take up the railway track and then I'll let the water in!'

When we are as young as eighteen we might well cry out in anguish, 'Oh for a chance to return to the thoughts of the truly unfettered mind!'

This conversation has most of the ingredients that could both impede our progress and accelerate it beyond our dreams. The scathing 'idiot child' put down by the 'experienced' elder, the confidence of the innovator that what he or she proposes *can* be done, of course. Finally perhaps, the turning from '*We'll* take up the track' to '*I'll* let the water in.' Never mind where the water is to come from. *I* will arrange it. You don't think any bigger than that!

Remember too, that the more difficult the problem, the greater the challenge and the greater the call for effort. Never be afraid of having your mind taxed to its limits. There will be others to share the experience with you. Engineering is not a lonely profession. It can be seen as an adventure into the unknown more exciting than any science fiction. It can be viewed as a struggle against a common enemy be it the customer's 'impossible' demands, or the constant fight against corrosion and decay, or the competition from other companies, either at home or overseas.

Engineering is more than merely a paradox or a puzzle for human intellectual delight. It is a whole way of life. It is something you have to touch and feel and 'get amongst' and therefore it cannot always be put into words, much as I have tried to do so in this book.

Where we might be in a mere thirty years from now surpasses the imagination of most of us. But I will leave you with the words of Nikola Tesla, addressing the Institution of Electrical Engineers, London, in 1892:

Ere many generations pass, our machinery will be driven by a power obtainable at any point of the universe. This idea is not novel. Men have been led to it long ago by instinct or reason. It has been expressed in many ways, and in many places, in the history of old and new. We find it in the delightful myth of Antheus, who derives power from the earth; we find it among the subtle speculations of one of your splendid mathematicians, and in many hints and statements of thinkers of the present time. Throughout space there is energy. Is this energy static or kinetic? If static our hopes are in vain; if kinetic—and this we know it is, for certain—then it is a mere question of time when men will succeed in attaching their machinery to the very wheelwork of nature.

Contemplate also these figures: if you could slow down our own moon's rotation by 1% in 100 years, and use the resulting kinetic energy, you could generate about 50 million megawatts of power, enough to supply the earth with continuous power over that period. If you could do the same to one of Saturn's moons I doubt if the solar system would even notice so minute a change!

Go to it, even as Michael Faraday wrote in his diary, 'Let the imagination go, guiding it by judgement and principle but holding it in and directing it by *experiment*.'

Be inspired—it is all yours to have and to hold.

Suggestions for Further Reading

The items in the following list are not so much books as brochures and pamphlets issued by the most authoritative bodies in the engineering and educational worlds.

Careers in British Engineering (CL91)
published by The Engineering Careers Information Service and available from:
>Engineering Industry Training Board Publications,
>PO Box 75,
>Stockport,
>Cheshire SK4 1PH.

A Closer Look at Engineering (Free)
published by and available from:
>The Engineering Council,
>Canberra House,
>10–16 Maltravers Street,
>London WC2R 3ER.

Training Opportunities in Engineering (Free)
published annually in September and available from:
>Schools Liaison Service,
>Institution of Mechanical Engineers,
>Northgate Avenue,
>Bury St Edmunds,
>Suffolk IP32 6BN.

Electrical Engineering. Have you got what it takes? (Free)
published by and available from:
> Schools Liaison Service,
> The Institution of Electrical Engineers,
> Station House,
> Nightingale Road,
> Hitchin,
> Herts SG5 1RJ.

Women into Science and Engineering, Report of the National Conference of The Standing Conference on Schools' Science and Technology held on 17 November 1983
published by and available from:
> The Standing Conference on Schools' Science and
>   Technology,
> c/o The Institution of Mechanical Engineers,
> 1 Birdcage Walk,
> London SW1H 9JJ.

Hobsons Engineering Casebook (Recent graduates describe their current projects)
a Careers Research and Advisory Centre (CRAC) publication produced annually and available from:
> Hobsons Press,
> Bateman Street,
> Cambridge CB2 1LZ.

Making Electric Things Happen, by P. L. Taylor (1967)
published by:
> Educational Explorers Ltd,
> 11 Crown Street,
> Reading RG1 2TQ.

Index

Bold figures indicate main items